Golfing in Oregon

The *Complete* guide to
Oregon's golf facilities

fifth edition

by
Daniel MacMillan

Published by

M A C Productions
Golf Guides Since 1986

Copyright © 1995 by Daniel MacMillan

All rights reserved. The course layouts, map grids and format are all protected under United States copyright laws. Unlawful use of this material will result in prosecution to the full extent of the law. No part of this publication may be stored in a retrieval system or transmitted, in any form, or by any means, electronically, mechanically, by photocopying, recording, facsimile, or otherwise, without the prior written permission of the publisher and author.

Library of Congress Cataloging-in-Publication Data

Printed in Canada

Cover photos appear courtesy of:
Awbrey Glen Golf Club
Bend, Oregon (503) 388-8526

First Edition, April 1990
Second Edition, January 1992
Third Edition, March 1993
Fourth Edition, March 1994
Fifth Edition, March 1995

ISBN 1-878591-15-0

Published by:
Mac Productions
P.O. Box 655
Carnation, Washington 98014 USA
(206) 333-4641

Preface

In this the fifth edition of **"Golfing in Oregon"** I hope it will be the most complete golf guide in the state published to date. We have completely upgraded the book and added new features to help with planning your golf trips. The size is designed with the idea that the book will more easily fit in your glove box or golf bag. We have also provided small map inserts along with the driving directions to help you get to the golf facilities. As always you will find new courses, par 3's, and ranges just opened or due to open later in the season. Layouts, prices and yardage have been revised to reflect any changes that have occurred since last year. I hope you enjoy the book, see you on the links!

Acknowledgements

A special thanks to all the pros, owners and course managers who have been so helpful in providing us access to their courses and current information. Thanks to the Oregon Department of Transportation for the endless supply of maps needed in doing this project.

Jeff Shelley for his help and personal support on these projects.

Thanks to Bob Valentine and his personal touch on these projects over the years, Thanks Robert!!!

This book would not have been possible without the tremendous support of my entire family and my friends. I thank each and every one of them for the special interest they have shown in the golf books.

To my children Joshua Daniel and Sarah Gene for showing me what really is important in life.

Thanks to my loving wife Kristi Gene. Words cannot express the love and support she has given me on this project. I feel blessed to have a wife whom provided a loving, caring, Christ like atmosphere in which to produce this book in. Thanks Kristi Gene. Most importantly my Lord Jesus, for his gentle hand and firm grip with my life and this company.

Daniel

Daniel MacMillan has been an avid golfer for the past 10 years. He enjoys researching and playing the various golf courses of the Pacific Northwest (if it were only that easy!!). *Golfing in Washington* was the brainchild of Daniel and his previous partner Mark Fouty who, one day while playing a round at Snohomish Golf Course, discussed finding a guide to use themselves. When no such guide was available this one was written. The book has taken on many stages. It was originally called *Golfing in Western Washington*, which encompassed only the more populous half of the state. In 1988 it expanded to *Golfing in Washington* (now in it's ninth edition). Meanwhile Mark pursued a career in New York so Daniel bought out Mark's share of the company. The company has therefore become a real family operation. Daniel drags his wife Kristi and their two children throughout the Pacific Northwest seeking information on new courses and facilities for upcoming publications. We hope all the thousands of miles and endless phone calls have paid off. This guide is designed to have all the information a golfer wants and needs to know about playing a course, and as a golfer Daniel has done just that.

Golfing in Oregon is the second book published by Mac Productions and written by Daniel. Now in its fifth edition it also is published on an annual basis. This book too has taken many forms it was originally called *Golfing in Oregon & Idaho*. In 1992 the book was changed to reflect the new format and now only includes the state of Oregon.

Golfing in British Columbia and *Golfing in Idaho & Montana* will be released in October of 1995. The books will be available in your local book stores or off course pro shops. New territories are always being explored for writing golf course guides such as this. Currently 6 more are in the works with many more in the initial planning stage. Look for the new publications at a pro shop or book store near you. Daniel's hope is that you will find this to be the best golf guide of its kind on the shelf.

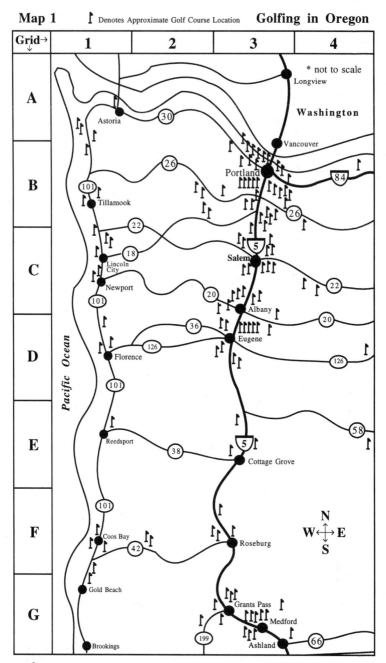

Map 1   ⚑ Denotes Approximate Golf Course Location   **Golfing in Oregon**

Map 2 Denotes Approximate Golf Course Location **Golfing in Oregon**

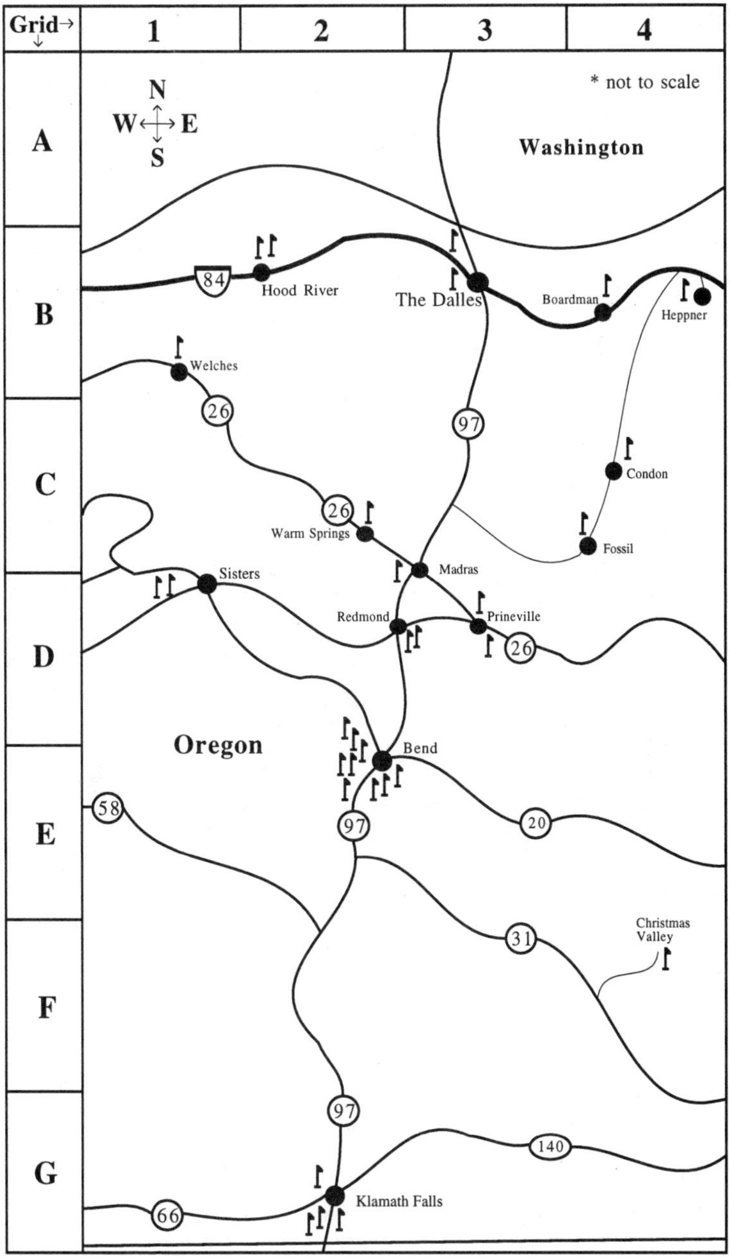
Grid→
1
2
3
4
A
B
C
D
E
F
G
N
W
E
S
* not to scale
Washington
84
Hood River
The Dalles
Boardman
Heppner
Welches
26
97
Condon
Warm Springs
Fossil
Madras
Sisters
Redmond
Prineville
26
Oregon
Bend
58
97
20
31
Christmas Valley
97
140
66
Klamath Falls

Map 3

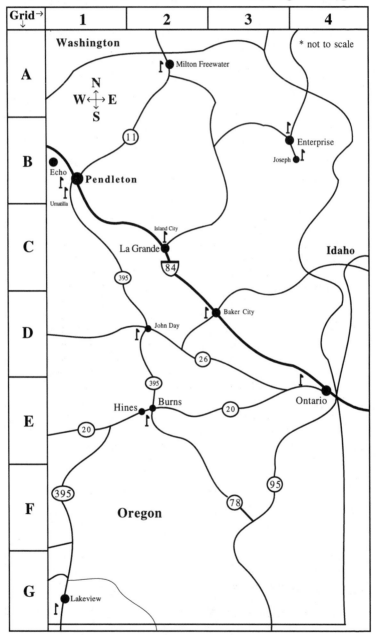

Map 3 ⚑ Denotes Approximate Golf Course Location   **Golfing in Oregon**

Grid →
↓

| 1 | 2 | 3 | 4 |

Washington

A

⚑ ● Milton Freewater

N
W ←↕→ E
S

⑪

B

● Echo

⚑ ● **Pendleton**

Umatilla

⚑ ● Enterprise
Joseph ⚑ ●

Island City

C

La Grande ●

③⑨⑤

84

Idaho

D

⚑ ● Baker City

John Day ⚑ ●

②⑥

E

③⑨⑤

Hines ● ⚑ ● Burns

②⓪

②⓪ ● Ontario

F

③⑨⑤

Oregon

⑦⑧

⑨⑤

G

⚑ ● Lakeview

* not to scale

Abbreviations, Explanatory notes and Disclaimers

Executive Course-An executive course is usually longer than a typical par 3 short course but shorter than a regulation course.

Private Course- A course that is not open to public play.

Semi-private- courses are closed to the public at certain times during the week.

T-Tour; **C**-Championship; **M**-Men; **W**-Women.

W/D-Weekday; **W/E**-Weekend.

N/A-Not available.

Course rating-This rates the degree of difficulty of course in the NW and refers to the average number of shots per round a scratch golfer ought to shoot. It is figured by rating teams who factor in terrain, length and hazards of each course. The higher the rating the more difficult the course. Course ratings courtesy of the *Pacific Northwest Golf Association & Oregon Golf Association.*

Slope-This is similar to the course rating but it considers other factors as well. The slope rating takes into consideration the playing difficulty of a course for handicaps above scratch. The higher the number, the more difficult the course. Slope ratings courtesy of the *Pacific Northwest Golf Association & Oregon Golf Association.*

Greens fee- prices are subject to change at any time. Because a number of Eastern Oregon courses close for the winter, the prices may reflect those of last year. When two prices are given, the first refers to the 18 hole fee, the second to the 9 hole fee. "Reciprocates" refers to the practice of private courses allowing members of other private courses to play their courses. However, because some courses only reciprocate with a limited number of other courses, it's best to call first.

Trail fee- the fee a course charges an individual to use their own power cart on the course.

Reservation policy- This refers to the maximum number of days the course allows reservations to made in advance under normal circumstances.

Winter condition- Dry, damp, wet refers to the club pro's opinion of the course's condition in rainy conditions.

Terrain- flat, flat some hills, relatively hilly, very hilly.

Tees- Grass or mats are the alternatives.

Temp. greens- When "yes" is stated, one *may* find some greens either under repair or susceptible to damage during inclement weather, thus a temporary in play.

Course layouts/yardage- My intent is to show tees in relation to greens, obvious hazards and other holes. Some hazards may not be adequately represented, nor are trees shown.

Agate Beach Golf Course (public)
4100 North Coast Highway; Newport, OR 97365; (503) 265-7331
Pro: William R. Martin, PGA. 9 hole course, driving range.
Rating/Slope: M 65.8/109;W 68.7/109. **Course record:** 62.
Greens fee: $24/$12 all week long; M/C, VISA.
Power cart: $20/$10. **Pull cart:** $1.50. **Trail fee:** $3/$6.
Reservation policy: yes, 7 days in advance, except for groups.
Winter condition: the course is open, very dry and drains well. **Terrain:** flat,
some hills. **Tees:** grass.**Temporary greens:** no. **Services:** club rentals, lessons,
restaurant, beer, wine, pro shop, driving range. **Comments:** Well maintained
course, excellent drainage for winter play. Easy to walk, picturesque course that
is a favorite for weekenders on the Oregon Coast. The golf course is open all year.

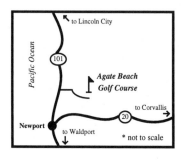

Directions: the golf course is located at
the north end of Newport Oregon on the
east side of Hwy 101, one mile north of
the Fred Meyer shopping center. Look for
signs marking your way to the golf course.

Course Yardage & Par:
M-3002 yards, par 36.
W-2894 yards, par 38.

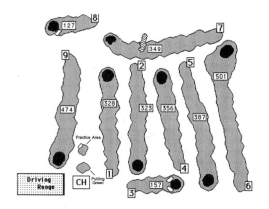

Alderbrook Golf Course (public)
7300 Alderbrook Road; Tillamook, OR 97141; (503) 842-6413
Owner: Neil Abrahamson. Pro: Steve Wilkes, PGA. 18 hole course.
Rating/Slope: M 66.5/107;W 70/109. **Course record:** 62.
Greens fee: $18/$10 summer, $15/$8 winter; Jr rates; M/C, VISA, DIS.
Power cart: $15/$8. **Pull cart:** $2. **Trail fee:** $4.
Reservation policy: yes, please call ahead for tee time reservations.
Winter condition: golf course is open. **Terrain:** flat, some hills. **Tees:** grass.
Temporary greens: no. **Services:** club rentals, snack bar, beer, wine, pro shop.
Comments: mature trees line the fairways of this excellent par 69 layout. A creek comes into play on several holes throughout the course. Excellent golf course to play while visiting the scenic and beautiful Oregon Coast.

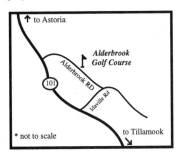

Directions: course is located 4 miles north of Tillamook off of Hwy 101. Proceed 4 miles north on Hwy 101 and go east on Alderbrook Road (just north of the cheese factory). When you come to a fork in the road stay left. The golf course will be on your right, 1.9 miles ahead. Look for a sign marking your way to the golf course.

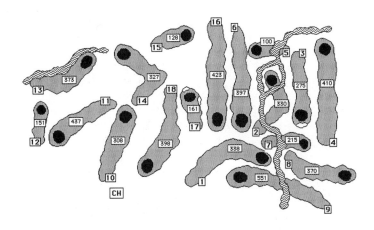

Course Yardage & Par:
M-5692 yards, par 66; W-5272 yards, par 71.

Alpine Meadows Golf Course (public)

PO Box 238; Golf Course Road; Enterprise, OR 97828; (503) 426-3246
Manager/Pro: Jim Chestnut. 9 hole course, dual tees for 18 holes.
Rating/Slope: M 66.8/113;W 69.9/116. **Course record:** 65.
Greens fee: $14/$8 all week long; no credit cards.
Power cart: $18/$10. **Pull cart:** $3/$1.50. **Trail fee:** no charge.
Reservation policy: no. **Winter condition:** the course is closed from October
15th to April 1st. **Terrain:** flat, some hills. **Tees:** grass. **Temporary greens:** no.
Services: club rentals, lessons, snack bar, lounge, beer, wine, liquor, pro shop.
Comments: Beautiful setting in the Wallowa Mountains. Greens are kept in
excellent condition throughout the peak season. Dual tee system for 18 hole play.

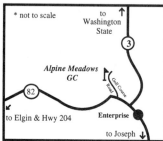

Directions: from Hwy 82 turn north
on Golf Course Road (the road between
the Safeway store and Burger Barn).
Proceed to the golf course, which will be
on your left hand side. The golf course is
located on the west end of the city. Look
for signs marking your turn to the course.

Course Yardage & Par:
M-3033 yards, par 36.
W-2806 yards, par 38.
Dual tees 18 holes:
M-6060 yards, par 72.
W-5620 yards, par 75.

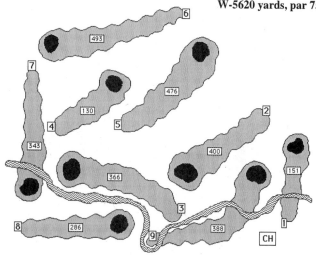

Arrowhead Golf Club (private)

28301 S Hwy 213; Molalla, OR 97038; (503) 655-1441 or (503) 829-8080
Director of Golf: Joe Clarizio. Pro: Rob Gibbons, PGA. 18 hole course.
Rating/Slope: C 70.5/123; M 68.7/119;W 69.4/106. **Course record:** 67.
Greens fee: private, members only; reciprocates. **Power cart:** private club.
Pull cart: private. **Trail fee:** private. **Reservation policy:** one week in advance.
Winter condition: wet. **Terrain:** flat. **Tees:** grass. **Temporary greens:** N/A.
Services: club rentals, lessons, snack bar, restaurant, lounge, beer, wine, liquor, pro shop, lockers, driving range. **Comments:** Situated along the banks of the Molalla River. A peaceful country club atmosphere. The driving range is open to the public. Good private facility with well conditioned greens and fairways.

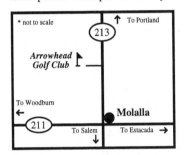

Directions: from I-205 N&S take exit #10 (Hwy 213) to Molalla, Oregon. From here proceed southbound on Hwy 213 for 14 miles. The golf course will be located on your right hand side when traveling southbound on Hwy 213. Look for a sign indicating your turn into the parking lot.

Course Yardage & Par:
C-6414 yards, par 72.
M-6038 yards, par 72.
W-5338 yards, par 73.

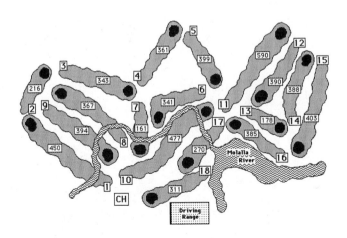

Astoria Golf & Country Club (private)
Route 1, Box 536; Hwy 101; Warrenton, OR 97146; (503) 861-2545
Pro: Mike Gove, PGA. 18 hole course, driving range.
Rating/Slope: C 71.0/120; M 70.4/118;W 72.8/115. **Course record:** 63.
Greens fee: private club, members and guests only, reciprocates.
Power cart: private club members only. **Pull cart:** private club members only.
Trail fee: personal carts are not allowed. **Reservation policy:** yes from May
1st to September 30th after 1:30pm. **Winter condition:** course is open weather
permitting. **Terrain:** relatively hilly. **Tees:** grass. **Temporary greens:** no.
Services: club rentals, lessons, restaurant, lounge, beer, wine, liquor, pro shop,
lockers, showers, driving range. **Comments:** Beautiful course located on the
Oregon Coast. Course is in kept in excellent condition throughout the year.

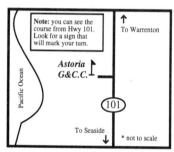

Directions: from Hwy 101 the course
is located at the south end of Warrenton Oregon. From Hwy 101 on the
west side of the Hwy look for a blue &
white sign marking the entrance to the
golf course. **Note:** the golf course can
be seen from Hwy 101.

Course Yardage & Par:
C-6488 yards, par 72.
M-6380 yards, par 72.
W-5893 yards, par 74.

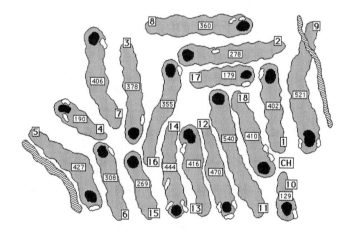

Auburn Center Golf Club (public)
5220 Center Street NE; Salem, OR 97301; (503) 363-4404
Managers: Gregg & Cindy Smith. 9 hole executive course, dual tees 18 holes.
Rating/Slope: the golf course is not rated. **Course record**: 27.
Greens fee: $10/$6 all week long; Jr. and Sr. rates; no credit cards.
Power cart: no power carts available. **Pull cart**: $1.50. **Trail fee**: not allowed.
Reservation policy: no reservations are needed. **Winter condition**: wet, open.
Terrain: flat, easy walking golf course. **Tees**: grass. **Temporary greens**: no.
Services: club rentals, snack bar, miniature golf, game room, putting green.
Comments: Flat course, very easy to walk. Course is excellent for beginners
and seniors. Good course for those wanting to practice thier short game on.

Directions: from I-5 S, take Market St.
exit #256 and go east to Lancaster Dr. Go
south (right) on Lancaster Dr. to Center
St. and turn left. The golf course is
located 1.1 miles ahead on Center St. The
golf course will be on your right hand
side. I-5N take Mission St exit #253 and
go east on Mission St. (N Santiam Hwy).
to Lancaster Dr. and proceed north on
Lancaster Dr. to Center St. Turn right on
Center St and follow to the golf course.

Course Yardage & Par:
M-1338 yards, par 29; W-1338 yards, par 29.
M-2708 yards, par 59; W-2708 yards, par 59.

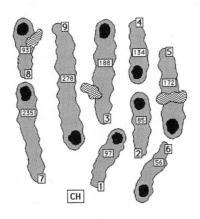

Awbrey Glen Golf Club (private, limited outside play)

2500 N.W. Awbrey Glen Drive; Bend, OR 97701; (503) 388-8526
Pro: Mark Amberson, PGA. 18 hole course, five hole par 3 learning center.
Rating/Slope: T 73.7/135; C71.9/132; M 69.6/124; W 69.6/119.
Greens fee: private club, (limited outside play call up to 3 days in advance).
Power cart: required until 1pm, $25. **Pull cart:** $4. **Trail fee:** not allowed.
Reservation policy: members 2 weeks. **Winter condition:** closed in winter.
Terrain: flat, rolling hills. **Tees:** grass. **Services:** club rentals, lessons, snack bar,
beer, wine, lockers, pro shop, restaurant, lounge, caddies, driving range.
Comments: this spectacular Bunny Mason design features the finest learning
centers in the NW. The double ended range is surrounded by a 5 hole par 3 course.
This course if you are able is a must play. Call for outside play policies.

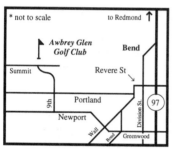

Directions: from Hwy 97 (3rd St.), turn
west on Greenwood (turns to Newport),
continue on Shevlin Park Road. Proceed
to Mt. Washington Dr. and turn right.
Proceed to Awbrey Glen Drive and
turn left. Proceed to the golf course.

Course Yardage & Par:
Tour: 7007 yards, par 72.
Championship: 6619 yards, par 72.
Members: 6160 yards, par 72.
Challenge: 5389 yards, par 72.

Course Yardage & Par:
"Awbrey Loop"
598 yards, par 15.

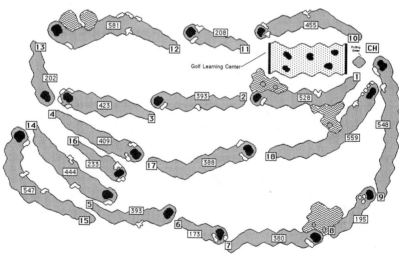

Baker Golf Club (public)
2801 Indiana Avenue; Baker City, OR 97814; (503) 523-2358
Pro: Bob Spencer. 9 hole course, dual tees for 18 holes.
Rating/Slope: M 68.7/103; W 70.0/109. **Course Record:** 62.
Greens fee: $15/$9 all week long; Jr. rates; M/C, VISA.
Power cart: $18/$9. **Pull cart:** $2/$1. **Trail fee:** no charge.
Reservation policy: no. **Winter condition:** the golf course is closed from
November from15th to March 1st. **Terrain:** flat, some hills. **Tees:** grass.
Temporary greens: none. **Services:** club rentals, lessons, lounge, beer, wine,
liquor, pro shop. **Comments:** the course is relatively short with wide open
fairways, small tricky greens and rolling terrain. Picturesque setting with moun-
tain views from many of the teeing areas. The course sports a dual set of tees.

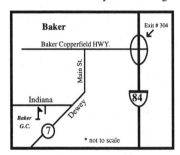

Directions: off of I-84 exit at City Center
(Elm Street) #304. Follow Hwy 7 towards
Sumpter. Turn right on Indiana Ave. (look
for a sign). The golf course is located at
the top of the hill on your left hand side.

Course Yardage & Par:
M-3018 yards, par 35.
W-2926 yards, par 38.
Dual Tees 18 holes:
M-6116 yards, par 70.
W-5932 yards, par 70.

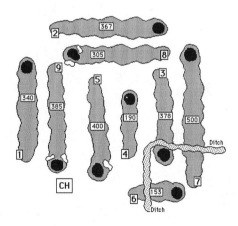

Bandon Face Rock Golf Course (public)
3235 Beach Loop Drive; Bandon, OR 97411; (503) 347-3818
Manager: Jerried Brown. 9 hole executive course, dual tees for 18 holes.
Rating/Slope: M 59.64/99 W 59.9/102. **Course record: 28.**
Greens fee: W/D $13/$8; W/E $14/$9; Jr. rates; credit cards are welcome.
Power cart: $13/$8. **Pull cart:** $2. **Trail fee:** $5. **Reservation policy:** not needed.
Winter condition: course is open, dry. **Terrain:** flat, easy walking course.
Tees: grass. **Temporary greens:** no. **Services:** club rentals, lessons, snack bar,
small pro shop. **Comments:** 9 holes along the scenic Johnson Creek. Golf course
is located next to the ocean in a valley protected from the wind. Excellent walking
golf course for the senior or first time golfer. Good public golf course.

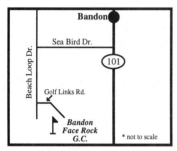

Directions: Course located in the south
end of Bandon. From Hwy 101, go west
on Sea Bird Drive to Beach Loop Road.
At Beach Loop Drive turn left and travel
2.2 miles to the golf course which will be
on your left. The golf course is located on
the south side of the Inn at Face Rock.
Look for signs the way is well marked.

Course Yardage & Par:
M-2045 yards, par 32.
W-1901 yards, par 32.
Dual Tees 18 holes:
M-4151 yards, par 64.
W-3802 yards, par 64.

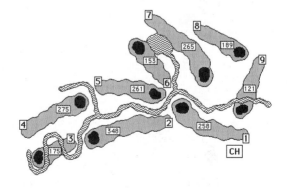

Battle Creek Golf Course (public)
6161 Commercial Street SE; Salem, OR 97306; (503) 585-1402
Pro: C. Lynn Baxter, PGA. 18 hole course, putting green.
Rating/Slope: C 67.4/109; M 64.6/102; W 67.7/109. **Course record:** 64.
Greens fee: W/D $19/$10; W/E $22/$13; M/C, VISA.
Power cart: $20/$10. **Pull cart:** $2. **Trail fee:** $8.
Reservation policy: yes, for Saturday and Sunday only. **Winter condition:** open.
Terrain: flat. **Tees:** grass. **Temporary greens:** yes. **Services:** club rentals,
lessons, caddy shack, restaurant, lounge, beer, wine, liquor, pro shop, lockers.
Comments: Challenging golf course with small elevated greens. Good drainage
makes this golf course very playable in the winter months. Excellent course.

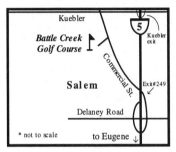

Directions: I-5S. Take Kuebler exit.
Keep right to Commercial St. Take a left
on Commercial follow for 1 mile to the
course on your left. I-5N. Take Salem exit
#249. Follow road for approximately 1
mile. The golf course will be located on
your left hand side. Course is located at
the south end of Salem. Look for signs.

Course yardage & Par:
C-5965 yards, par 72.
M-5340 yards, par 72.
W-4935 yards, par 72.

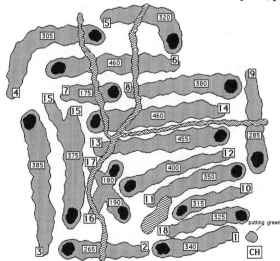

Bayou Golf Club (public)
9301 SW Bayou Drive; McMinnville, OR 97128; (503) 472-4651
Pro: Sarah Bakefelt. 9 hole regulation course , 9 hole par 3 course.
Rating/Slope: C 69.5/108; M 67.8/106;W 68.2/104. **Course record: 64.**
Greens fee: W/D$16/$8; W/E $20/$10; Jr. and Sr. rates, no credit cards.
Power cart: $18/$10. **Pull cart:** $3/$2. **Trail fee:** $9/$5.
Reservation policy: yes, for Saturday, Sunday and Holidays only.
Winter condition: open, fair. **Terrain:** gentle rolling hills. **Tees:** grass.
Temporary greens: no. **Services:** club rentals, lessons, snack bar, beer,
wine, pro shop, driving range. **Comments:** Course was built in 1964. Riverside
setting with water hazards coming into play on all 9 holes. Good test of golf.

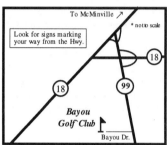

Directions: the golf course located is
1.25 miles southwest of McMinnville
Oregon on Hwy 99W. Look for a large
sign on the Hwy. If on Hwy 18 watch
for signs for Hwy 99W southbound and
follow to the golf course which will be
on your right hand side.

Course Yardage & Par:
C-3166 yards, par 36.
M-3016 yards, par 36.
W-2550 yards, par 36.

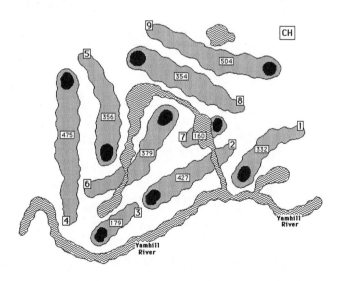

Bear Creek Golf Course (public)
2355 S Pacific Highway; Medford, OR 97501; (503) 773-1822
Pro: Guy Hupe, PGA. 9 hole executive course, covered driving range.
Rating/Slope: the golf course is not rated. **Course record:** 25.
Greens fee: W/D$11.50/$7; W/E $13/$8. **Power cart:** none. **Pull cart:** $1.25.
Trail fee: not allowed. **Reservation policy:** reservations are not needed.
Winter condition: course is open. **Terrain:** flat, some hills. **Tees:** grass.
Temporary greens: no. **Services:** club rentals, lessons, snack bar, beer, wine,
pro shop, covered driving range, 18 hole miniature course. **Comments:** Very
popular complex. Facility is kept in excellent shape during the peak season. Great
course to take the family or first time golfer to. Water is a factor on half the holes.

Directions: from I-5 northbound &
southbound use exit #27 to Barnett Rd.
Proceed to Hwy 99 (Pacific Hwy). Turn
south on Pacific Hwy and proceed for 3/4
of a mile to the golf course. The golf course
will be located on your left hand side. The
golf course has great freeway access. Look
for signs marking your way. The route is
well indicated.

Course Yardage & Par:
M-1509 yards, par 28.
W-1509 yards, par 30.

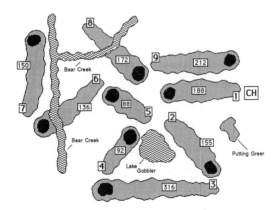

Bend Golf & Country Club (private)
20399 Murphy Road; Bend, OR 97702; (503) 382-7437
Pro: Jim Wilkinson, PGA. 18 hole course, driving range.
Rating/Slope: C 73.8/132; M 71.4/127; W 72.5/129. **Course record:** 65.
Greens fee: private club, members & guests only, reciprocates ; M/C, VISA.
Power cart: private club. **Pull cart:** private club. **Trail fee:** not allowed.
Reservation policy: private club members only. **Winter condition:** course is
closed in winter from November to thaw. **Terrain:** flat, some hills. **Tees:** grass.
Temporary greens: no. **Services:** club rentals, lessons, snack bar, lounge, beer,
wine, liquor, pro shop, lockers, showers, driving range. **Comments:** Tree lined
fairways and views of the Three Sisters Mtn.'s add to this well kept country club.

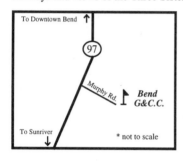

Directions: from Hwy 97 turn on
Murphy Road and proceed eastbound.
Follow Murphy Road for 3/4 of a mile to
Country Club Drive. The golf course will
be just ahead on your right hand side.

Course Yardage & Par:
C-6851 yards, par 72.
M-6441 yards, par 72.
W-6004 yards, par 75.

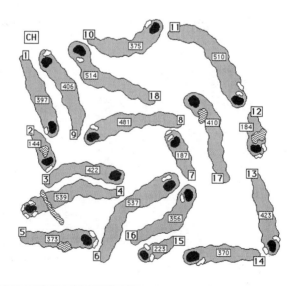

Black Butte Ranch (semi-private resort) Big Meadow Course

**Box 8000; Hwy 20; Sisters, OR 97759; (503) 595-6689, 800-399-2322 for times.
Director of Golf/Head Pro: JD Mowlds,PGA. 18 hole course, range.
Rating/Slope**: C 72.0/127; M 70.0/124; W 70.5/115. **Course record:** 65.
Greens fee: $49/$29; M/C, VISA, AMEX. **Power cart:** $28/$17. **Pull cart:** $3/$2.
Trail fee: not allowed. **Reservation policy:** Ranch Guests W/D 24 hours in
advance, for W/E, Monday prior to W/E. Non guests Thursday, prior to the W/E.
Winter condition: closed late October to mid March. **Terrain:** flat, some hills.
Tees: grass. **Temporary greens:** no. **Services:** club rentals, lessons, snack bar,
beer, wine, pro shop, driving range. **Comments:** excellent facility. Great views
of the nearby mountains and forests. Great vacation spot for the whole family.

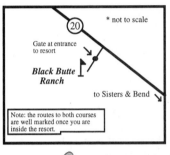

* not to scale

Gate at entrance
to resort

*Black Butte
Ranch*

to Sisters & Bend

Note: the routes to both courses
are well marked once you are
inside the resort.

Directions: the golf course is located 7
miles west of Sisters Oregon on Hwy 20.
The turn for the Black Butte Ranch is well
marked. Once inside the complex the route
to the golf course has plenty of signs to
mark your way. Look for the signs that
say Hawks Beard it runs throughout the
complex.

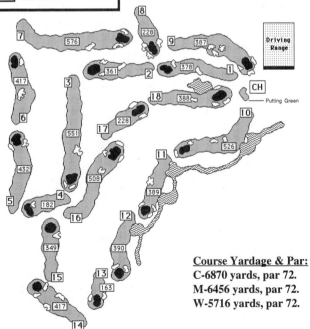

Course Yardage & Par:
C-6870 yards, par 72.
M-6456 yards, par 72.
W-5716 yards, par 72.

Black Butte Ranch (semi-private resort) Glaze Meadow Course

Box 8000; Hwy 20; Sisters, OR 97759; (503) 595-6400, 800-399-2322 for times.
Director of Golf/Head Pro: JD Mowlds, PGA. 18 hole course, range.
Rating/Slope: C 71.5/128; M 69.9/124;W 72.1/120. **Course record:** 65.
Greens fee: $49/$29; M/C, VISA, AMEX. **Power cart:** $28/$17. **Pull cart:** $3/$2.
Trail fee: not allowed. **Reservation policy:** Ranch Guests W/D 24 hours in
advance, W/E Monday prior to W/E. Non guests Thursday prior to the W/E.
Winter condition: closed from late October to mid March. **Terrain:** flat, some
hills. **Tees:** grass. **Temporary greens:** no. **Services:** club rentals, lessons, snack
bar, beer, wine, pro shop, driving range. **Comments:** excellent facility. Great shot
makers course. This golf course and vaction spot is worth a special trip. Bring the
whole family.

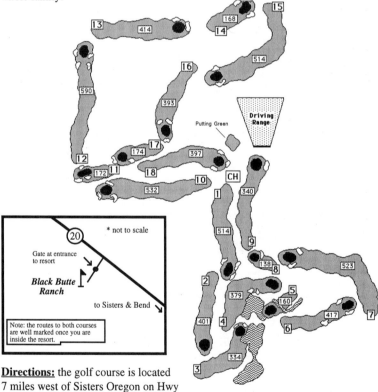

Directions: the golf course is located
7 miles west of Sisters Oregon on Hwy
20.The turn for the Black Butte Ranch
is well marked. Once inside the complex
the route to the golf course has plenty
of signs to mark your way.

Course yardage & Par:
C-6560 yards, par 72.
M-6266 yards, par 72.
W-5616 yards, par 72.

Broadmoor Golf Course (public)

3509 NE Columbia Boulevard; Portland, OR 97211; (503) 281-1337
Pro: Scott Krieger, PGA. 18 hole course, driving range.
Rating/Slope: C 70.2/122; M 68.4/116; W 69.9/110. **Course record:** 64.
Greens fee: W/D $18/$9; W/E $20/$10; M/C, VISA for merchandise only.
Power cart: $20/$10. **Pull cart:** $2. **Trail fee:** not allowed.
Reservation policy: yes, call Friday for the following week and weekend.
Winter condition: open. **Terrain:** flat, some hills. **Tees:** grass.
Temporary greens: no. **Services:** club rentals, lessons, restaurant, beer, wine, pro shop, driving range. **Comments:** Beautiful tree lined course with water and sand coming into play on several holes. Portland's most popular public golf course.

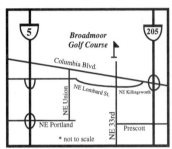

Directions: from I-5 N&S take the Columbia Street exit and proceed eastbound for 1 mile to NE 33rd. Turn left to the golf course. From I-205 N&S take the Columbia Street exit and proceed westbound for 2 miles to the golf course which will be on your left hand side.

Course Yardage & Par:
C-6498 yards, par 72.
M-5966 yards, par 72.
W-5384 yards, par 74.

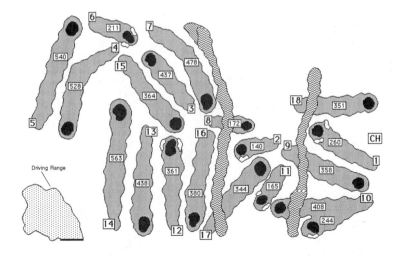

Broken Top (private)
61999 Broken Top Drive; Bend OR 97702; (503)383-0868.
Pro: Randy Shannon, PGA. 18 hole course, driving range, putting course.
Rating/Slope: T 74.4/138; C 71.5/130; M 68.8/121; W 70.3/122.
Greens fee: private club, members & guests; pro reciprocation on a limited basis.
Power cart: private club. **Pull cart:** no. **Trail fee:** persoanl carts are not allowed.
Reservation policy: private club. **Winter condition:** as dictated by weather.
Terrain: flat, some hills. **Tees:** bent. **Services:** full service private country club.
Comments: this Tom Weiskopf, Jay Moorish designed golf course opened in
July of 1993. The par 4, 364 yard, 11th is the course's signature hole. The course
features classic championship design that plays over 7100 yards from the back tees.

Directions: from Hwy 97 turn westbound
to Division. Proceed to Colorado. Turn
westbound and proceed to Century Drive.
Proceed westbound on Century Drive to
Mount Washington. Proceed northbound
on Mount Washington to Broken Top.
Look for signs marking your way.

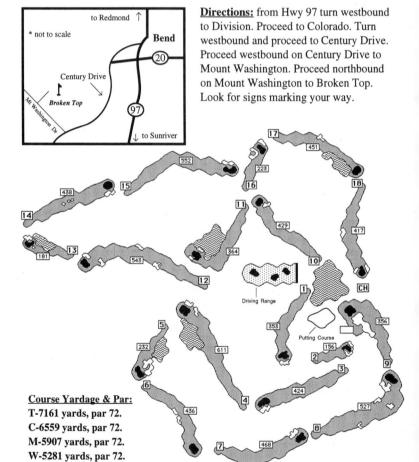

Course Yardage & Par:
T-7161 yards, par 72.
C-6559 yards, par 72.
M-5907 yards, par 72.
W-5281 yards, par 72.

Cedar Bend Golf Club (public)
34391 Squaw Valley Road; Gold Beach, OR 97444; (503) 247-6911
Manager: Kathy Allison. 9 hole course, dual tees for 18 holes.
Rating/Slope: M 69.2/117; W 67.6/115. **Course record**: 67.
Greens fee: $18/$12 all week long; Jr. and Sr. rates; M/C, VISA.
Power cart: $15/$10. **Pull cart:** $1. **Trail fee:** $5.
Reservation policy: yes, call in advance for tee times. A must during the summer.
Winter condition: damp. **Terrain:** flat. **Tees:** grass. **Temporary greens:** no.
Services: club rentals, lessons, snack bar, lounge, beer, wine, liquor, pro shop,
driving range. **Comments:** Streams, lush fairways and well kept greens add to
your game at this course. The golf course is flat and very easy to walk.

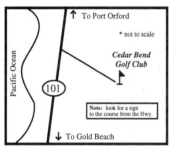

Directions: the golf course is located 12
miles north of Gold Beach and 14 miles
south of Port Orford. **Note:** look for a
sign on Hwy 101 for your turn to the golf
course which is located 3 miles inland.

Course Yardage & Par:
M-3000 yards, par 36.
W-2605 yards, par 37.
Dual tees 18 holes:
M-6025 yards, par 72.
W-5305 yards, par 74.

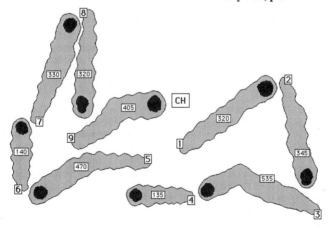

Cedar Links (public)
3155 Cedar Links Drive; Medford, OR 97501; (503) 773-4373
Pro: Scott Lusk, PGA. 18 hole course, driving range.
Rating/Slope: C 68.9/114; M 67.7/112; W 68.7/112. **Course record:** 63.
Greens fee: W/D $20/$12; W/E $20/$12; M/C, VISA.
Power cart: $18/$10. **Pull cart:** $3/$2. **Trail fee:** $12 (tournaments only).
Reservation policy: yes, 7 days in advance. **Winter condition:** open, dry.
Terrain: relatively hilly. **Tees:** grass. **Temporary greens:** in winter @ times.
Services: club rentals, lessons, snack bar, restaurant, lounge, beer, wine,
pro shop, driving range. **Comments:** Family owned public golf course in the
foothills of Medford. The golf course sports several water holes and tricky greens.

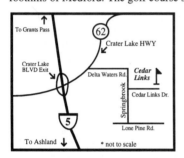

Directions: from I-5 N&S take Hwy 62
(Crater Lake Hwy) exit #30 and go north.
Turn right on Delta Waters Road. Proceed
to Springbrook and turn right. At Cedar
Links Drive, turn left to golf course which
is located on your left hand side. Look for
signs to the golf course the way is well
marked.

Course Yardage & Par:
C-6142 yards, par 70.
M-5893 yards, par 70.
W-5145 yards, par 71.

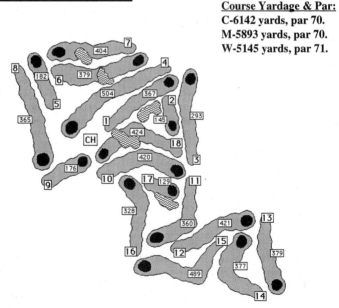

Charbonneau Golf & Country Club (public)

32020 Charbonneau Drive; Wilsonville, OR 97070; (503) 694-1246
Pro: to be determined. 27 hole executive course, driving range.
Rating/Slope: C 60.3/85; M 59.3/84;W 60.7/86. **Course record: 54.**
Greens fee: W/D $24/$18/$11*; W/E $26/$20/$12*; winter rates; M/C, VISA.
Power cart: $20/$10*. Pull cart: $2/$1*. Trail fee: not allowed. (*will change).
Reservation policy: yes, one week in advance. **Winter condition:** open, dry.
Terrain: flat, some slight hills. **Tees:** grass. **Temporary greens:** no.
Services: club rentals, lessons, restaurant, lounge, beer, wine, pro shop, range.
Comments: Beautiful executive course layout that gives all golfers a challenge.
The golf course can always be found in great shape. Worth a trip if in the area.

Directions: from I-5 N&S take Charbon-neau exit #282. Go east for approximately one mile to Charbonneau Village and proceed to the golf course. **Note:** Make sure you look for signs marking your way to the golf course.

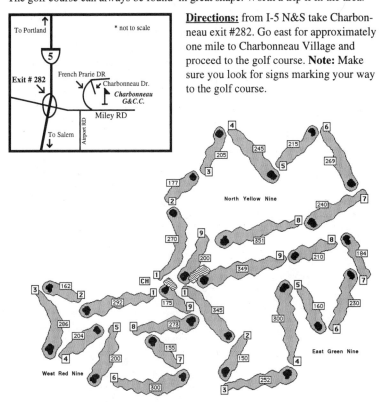

Course Yardage & Par:
North Yellow Nine: C-2172 yards, par 31; M-2026, par 31; W-1802, par 31.
East Green Nine: C-2180 yards, par 31; M-2111, par 31; W-1943, par 31.
West Red Nine: C-2047 yards, par 31; M-1936, par 31; W-1780, par 31.

Christmas Valley Golf Course (public)
PO Box 181; Christmas Valley, OR 97641; (503) 576-2216
Manager: Tony Meterick. 9 hole course, driving range.
Rating/Slope: the golf course is not rated. **Course record:** 34.
Greens fee: $15/$10 all week long; winter rates; M/C, VISA.
Power cart: $10. **Pull cart:** $2. **Trail fee:** not allowed.
Reservation policy: no. **Winter condition:** open, dry. **Terrain:** flat.
Tees: grass. **Temporary greens:** no. **Services:** club rentals, snack bar,
restaurant, lounge, beer, wine, liquor, pro shop, driving range, lodge.
Comments: golf course is challenging to all levels of golfers. Hazards such as
sand, water and sagebrush abound if you stray from the fairway. Good course.

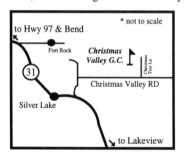

Directions: from Hwy 97 take Hwy 31
to Fort Rock/Christmas Valley exit.
Take Co. Rd. 5-10 to Co. Rd. 5-14.
5-14 will become Christmas Valley Rd.
at Christmas Valley. Follow Rd. to the
golf course. **Note:** Look for signs marking
your way to the golf course.

Course Yardage & Par:
C-3517 yards, par 36.
M-3393 yards, par 36.
W-3070 yards, par 38.

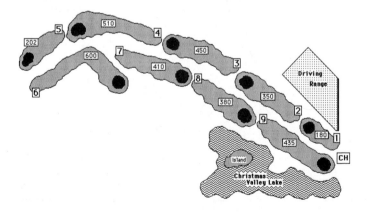

Circle Bar Golf Club (public)

48447 W Oak Road; PO Box 214; Oakridge, OR 97463; (503) 782-3541
Manager: Deanna Wellman. 9 hole course, dual tees for 18 holes.
Rating/Slope: M 70.8/119; W 73.0/118. **Course record:** 33.
Greens fee: W/D $12/$7; W/E $15/$9; no credit cards.
Power cart: $12/$7. **Pull cart:** $2. **Trail fee:** $6.
Reservation policy: yes, a must, please call ahead for a tee time.
Winter condition: wet, club house closed November 1st to March 1st.
Terrain: relatively hilly. **Tees:** grass. **Temporary greens:** no.
Services: club rentals, snack bar, beer, wine, pro shop, banquet facilities.
Comments: Club memberships available. Water comes into play on half the holes.
If you are looking for a course for a quick 9 holes on, try Circle Bar Golf Club.

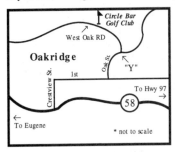

Directions: from Hwy 58 turn north on Crestview St. go across the train tracks to 1st. Turn right on 1st St and proceed to Oak St., turn left. Follow Oak St. to the "Y" in the road and turn left. This is West Oak RD. Follow this to the golf course. **Note:** Make sure you follow the signs marking your way.

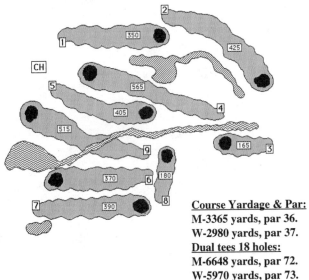

Course Yardage & Par:
M-3365 yards, par 36.
W-2980 yards, par 37.
Dual tees 18 holes:
M-6648 yards, par 72.
W-5970 yards, par 73.

Claremont Golf Club (public)

15955 NW West Union Road; Portland, OR 97229; (503) 690-4589
Pro: Steve Morrison. 9 hole course, dual tees for 18 holes.
Rating/Slope: C 68.6/116; M 66.0/109; W 70.4/114. **Record:** 33 (9 holes).
Greens fee: W/D $18/$10; W/E $22/$12; Sr. rates (M-F); VISA.
Power cart: none. **Pull cart:** $2. **Trail fee:** N/A. **Reservation policy:** yes, please
call 1 week in advance for tee times. **Winter condition:** open, course drains well.
Terrain: flat. **Tees:** grass. **Temporary greens:** no. **Services:** club rentals, pro shop.
Comments: excellent walking golf course. One of the finest 9 hole golf courses
to emerge in the Portland area. Water comes into play on several holes and can
make this course play difficult at times. Good test of golf for all abilities.

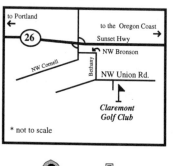

Directions: from Hwy 26 (Sunset Hwy)
take the Cornell/Bethany exit and turn
right at the 2nd stoplight (Bethany Blvd.)
Proceed to NW West Union Road and turn
left. The golf course is located at the top of
the hill on the right hand side.

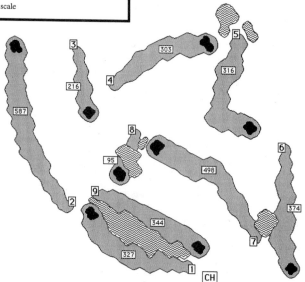

Course Yardage & Par: Dual Tees 18 holes:
C-3060 yards, par 36.   6120 yards, par 72.
M-2961 yards, par 36.   5922 yards, par 72.
W-2692 yards, par 36.   5384 yards, par 72.

Colonial Valley Golf Course (public)

75 Nelson Way; Grants Pass, OR 97526; (503) 479-5568
Pro: Randy Blankenship. 9 hole executive course.
Rating/Slope: M 29/126; W 31/no rating. **Course record:** 28.
Greens fee: $7 for nine holes, $4 for replay; no credit cards.
Power cart: none available. **Pull cart:** $1. **Trail fee:** not allowed.
Reservation policy: yes, groups of 12 or more, 1 week in advance.
Winter condition: wet, closed December 15th to February 1st. **Terrain:** flat.
Tees: grass. **Temporary greens:** no. **Services:** club rentals, lessons, snack bar,
lounge, beer, wine, pro shop. **Comments:** Best kept secret in Southern Oregon.
The course is in excellent condition. Good facility to practice your iron play on.

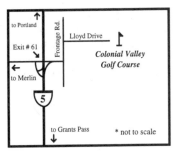

Directions: from I-5 N&S take Merlin
exit #61, and go east to Frontage Road.
Turn left and go north to Lloyd Drive and
turn right on Lloyd Drive. Proceed 1/2
mile to the golf course on your right.
Note: Look for signs marking your way
to the golf course.

Course Yardage & Par:
M-1587 yards, par 29; W-1587, par 31.

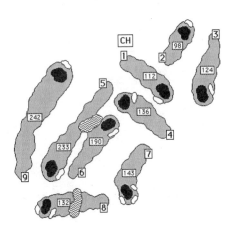

Columbia Edgewater Country Club (private)

2220 NE Marine Drive; Portland, OR 97211; (503) 285-8354
Pro: Dan Hixson, PGA. 18 hole course, driving range. Course record: 65.
Rating/Slope: T 72.9/131; C 71.1/128; M 69.6/124; W 73.7/129; W 71.5/125.
Greens fee: private club, members and guests only; reciprocates.
Power cart: private club. **Pull cart:** private club. **Trail fee:** not allowed.
Reservation policy: private club, 4 days in advance. **Winter condition:** open.
Terrain: flat, some hills. **Tees:** grass. **Temporary greens:** no. **Services:** lessons,
snack bar, restaurant, lounge, pro shop, driving range. **Comments:** old course built
on rolling flood plains in 1925. Recent renovations have been made toward the
original design. Host club of the Ping/Cellular One LPGA Tour event. Great course.

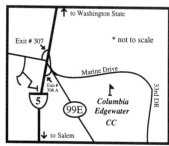

Directions: from I-5 N&S take Marine
Drive exit #306A and proceed eastbound
for .5 miles to the golf course. Look for a
sign to your turn to the golf course.

Course Yardage & Par:
T-6702 yards, par 71.
C-6342 yards, par 71.
M-6021 yards, par 71.
W-5762 yards, par 72.
W-5416 yards, par 72.

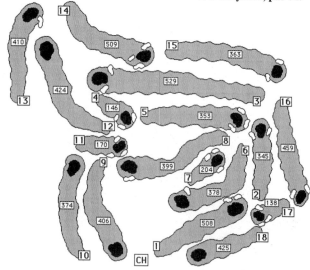

Colwood National Golf Club (public)

7313 NE Columbia Boulevard; Portland, OR 97218; (503) 254-5515
Pro: Dave Miller, PGA. 18 hole course.
Rating/Slope: M 69.1/115; W 71.5/111. **Course record**: 63.
Greens fee: W/D $16/$9; W/E $18/$10; Jr. rates.
Power cart: $20/$11. **Pull cart**: $3. **Trail fee**: $10/$5.50.
Reservation policy: 1 week in advance for foursomes playing 18 holes only.
Winter condition: dry. **Terrain:** flat. **Tees:** grass. **Temporary greens:** no.
Services: club rentals, lessons, restaurant, beer, wine, lounge, pro shop.
Comments: The course is noted for excellent conditioned greens and well kept
fairways. Great public golf course that can get very busy during the summer.

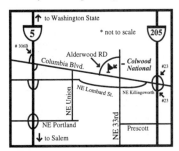

Directions: the golf course is located one
mile east of Broadmoor off Columbia
Boulevard. From I-5 northbound and
southbound take NE Columbia Blvd. exit.
Exit and go eastbound for 6.7 miles. The
golf course will be on your left hand side.
Look for signs indicating your turns to the
course the way is well marked.

Course Yardage & Par:
M-6277 yards, par 72.
W-5673 yards, par 77.

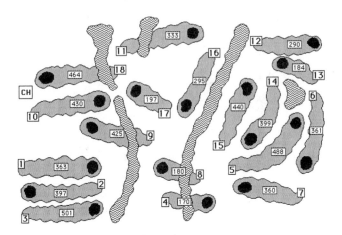

Condon Golf Course (public)
North Lincoln Street; Condon, OR 97823; (503) 384-4266
Pro: none. Manager: none. 9 hole course.
Rating/Slope: M 68.2/105; W 70.3/109. **Course record: 70.**
Greens fee: $6/$4, look for rates on the current rate sheet; no credit cards.
Power cart: power carts are not available. **Pull cart:** pull carts are not available.
Trail fee: not available. **Reservation policy:** prior reservations are not needed.
Winter condition: closed during the winter months. **Terrain:** flat, some hills.
Tees: grass. **Temporary greens:** no. **Services:** the golf course has very limited
services. **Comments:** Greens fee are often paid by the honor system. Golf course
is very easy to walk with rolling hills. The course lies on the NW edge of Condon.

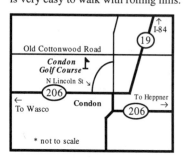

Directions: course is located off of Hwy
206 on North Lincoln St. in Condon. If
coming from Hwy 19 the golf course will
be located at the north end of the city of
Condon. **Note:** Be sure to look for a sign
on the Hwy marking the way to the golf
course.

Course Yardage & Par:
M-3111 yards, par 36.
W-3111 yards, par 36.

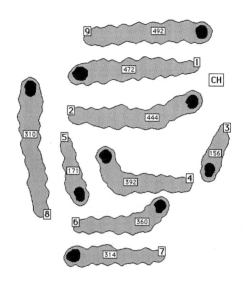

Coos Country Club (private)
999 Coos City-Sumner Road; Coos Bay, OR 97420; (503) 267-7257
Pro: Jim Bartleson, PGA. 9 hole course, dual tees for 18 holes.
Rating/Slope: M 68.6/122; W 71.3/123. **Course record: 63.**
Greens fee: private club; reciprocates; credit cards for merchandise only.
Power cart: private club. **Pull cart**: private club. **Trail fee**: not allowed.
Reservation policy: private club. **Winter condition**: open, wet.
Terrain: flat, some hills. **Tees**: grass. **Temporary greens**: no.
Services: club rentals, lessons, restaurant, beer, wine, liquor, pro shop, lockers,
showers, driving range. **Comments**: The course is short, yet very demanding.
Host of the Southwest Oregon Amateur every July 4th. Great golf course. This
private 9 hole course could be one of the finest 9 holer's in the state of Oregon.

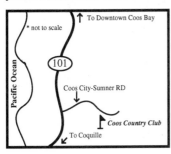

Directions: from Hwy 101 exit at Coos
City-Sumner Road. Proceed on Coos
City-Sumner Road for 1 mile to the
golf course. The golf course is located
approximately 5 miles south of the city
of Coos Bay.

Course Yardage & Par:
M-2921 yards, par 34.
W-2811 yards, par 36.
Dual Tees 18 holes:
M-5728 yards, par 68.
W-5547 yards, par 72.

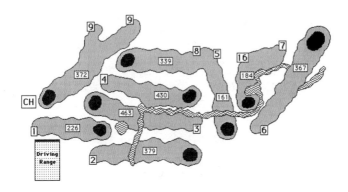

Coquille Valley Elks Golf Club (private)

PO Box 215 (Hwy 42); Myrtle Point, OR 97458; (503) 572-5367
Manager: Melissa Wise. 9 hole course, driving range.
Rating/Slope: C 63.2/103; M 62.5/101; W 66.0/103. **Course record:** 27.
Greens fee: private club; annual fees; non Elk guests $15.
Power cart: private club. **Pull cart:** private club. **Trail fee:** private club.
Reservation policy: no. **Winter condition:** open, wet. **Terrain:** flat, some hills.
Tees: grass. **Temporary greens:** no. **Services:** club rentals, restaurant, lounge,
beer, pro shop, driving range. **Comments:** The course is owned by the Coquille
Valley Elks Lodge #1935. Home of the State Elks tournament over Labor Day
weekend. Fairly good walking course with only one steep grade.

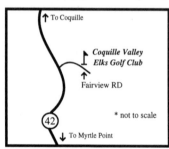

Directions: from I-5 N&S in Roseburg,
Oregon take the Coos Bay/Winston exit.
Proceed on Hwy 42 for approximately
50 miles west to the golf course. The
course is located half way between Myrtle
Point and Coquille. Your turn to the golf
course will be on Fairview Road. Look for
signs indicating your way to the course.

Course Yardage & Par
M-2216 yards, par 33; W-2165 yards, par 35.

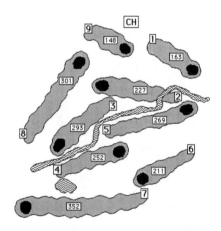

Corvallis Country Club (private)

1850 SW Whiteside Drive; Corvallis, OR 97333; (503) 752-3484
Pro: Todd G. Young, PGA. 18 hole course, driving range.
Rating/Slope: C 69.5/126; M 68.9/125; W 71.1/117. **Course record**: 64.
Greens fee: private; reciprocates need membership card; M/C, VISA.
Power cart: private club. **Pull cart:** private club. **Trail fee:** not allowed.
Reservation policy: yes, 6 days in advance. **Winter condition:** open, wet.
Terrain: relatively hilly. **Tees:** grass. **Temporary greens:** no.
Services: club rentals, lessons, snack bar, restaurant, beer, wine, liquor,
pro shop, driving range. **Comments:** The course is short, with small tricky
greens. Must play a position round of golf to score well. Good golf course.

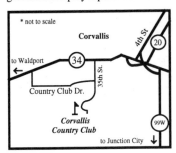

Directions: from I-5 N&S travel west
on Hwy 34 to Philomath Hwy. Turn left,
proceed to the 2nd light (35th St.), turn
left and follow the road to the clubhouse.

Course Yardage & Par:
C-6045 yards, par 71.
M-5825 yards, par 71.
W-5441 yards, par 74.

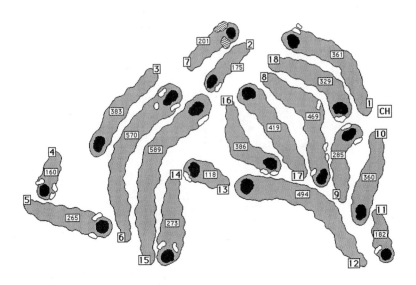

Creekside Golf Course (semi-private)

6250 Clubhouse Drive South; Salem, OR 97306; (503) 363-GOLF (4653)
Pro: Tom Ferrin, PGA. 18 hole course, driving range, putting green.
Rating/Slope: T 73.6/131; C 71.9/128; M 69.5/120; W 70.4/122. **Record:** 69.
Greens fee: $34/$18. **Power cart:** $20/$12. **Pull cart:** $2. **Trail fee:** not allowed.
Reservation policy: daily fee guests may call 5 days in advance. **Winter condition:** open, wet. **Terrain:** flat, some hills. **Tees:** grass. **Services:** club rentals, lessons, vending, beer, pro shop, driving range, Henry-Griffitts custom club fitting.
Comments: Course designed by Peter Jacobsen & Golf Services Group. Excellent new layout that will challenge you at every turn. This will be a very demanding layout from tee to green. This course opened for play in 1994 and is spectacular.

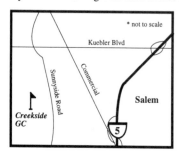

Directions: from I-5 N&S take the Kuebler exit in south Salem. Proceed west on Kuebler to Sunnyside Road. Turn south on Sunnyside Road for 1/2 mile to the golf course on the west side of the road.

Course Yardage & Par:
T-6942 yards, par 72.
C-6573 yards, par 72.
M-6010 yards, par 72.
W-5285 yards, par 72.

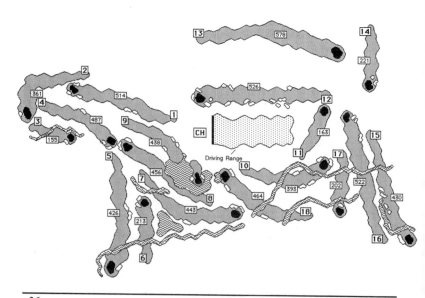

Crestview Hills Golf Course (public)

1680 Crestline Drive; Waldport, OR 97394; (503) 563-3020
Owners: Tim & Kathee Tarpley. Pro: John Erwin. 9 hole course.
Rating/Slope: M 66.0/111; W 69.5/114. **Course record: 32.**
Greens fee: W/D $16/$8; W/E $18/$9; M/C, VISA. **Power cart:** $18/$9.
Pull cart: $1. **Trail fee:** $9/$4.50. **Reservation policy:** yes, taken & suggested
June to September. **Winter condition:** course open, weather permitting.
Terrain: relatively hilly. **Tees:** grass. **Temporary greens:** no. **Services:** club
rentals, lessons, snack bar, beer, wine, pro shop. **Comments:** Beautiful par 36
golf course that sits on top of a hill and is out of the coastal wind and fog. Rolling
terrain will often result in some tricky lies from the fairway. Good family course.

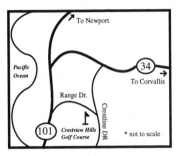

Directions: the course is located 1 mile
south of Waldport. From Hwy 101 turn
east on Range Drive (milepost 157) and
proceed 1 mile to the course entrance
on your right. Look for a sign marking
your turn to the golf course. The way is
well marked.

Course Yardage & Par:
C-2828 yards, par 36.
M-2728 yards, par 36.
W-2549 yards, par 36.

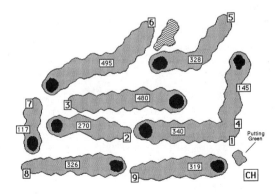

Crooked River Ranch Golf Course (public)

PO Box 1287; 5195 Clubhouse RD; Crooked River, OR 97760; (503) 923-6343
Pro: Gary L. Popp, PGA. 18 hole course. Course record: N/A.
Rating/Slope: M 64.7/100; W 65.9/102 (the course will be re rated).
Greens fee: $22/$14 everyday; winter & Jr. rates; M/C, VISA.
Power cart: $22/$15. **Pull cart:** $2. **Trail fee:** $7.50.
Reservation policy: yes, call Thursday noon, before the weekend for tee times.
Winter condition: the golf course is open weather permitting. **Terrain:** flat, some
hills. **Tees:** grass. **Temporary greens:** no. **Services:** club rentals, lessons, snack
bar, restaurant, lounge, beer, wine, liquor, pro shop, driving range, putting green.
Comments: Golf is played here all year long when most all the other Central Ore.
courses are snowed in. Great, scenic golf course. 18 holes are now open for play.

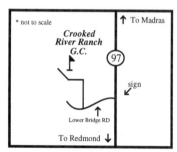

Directions: the golf course is located 7
miles from Hwy 97. Turn off of Hwy 97
at the Crooked River Ranch signs which
are located on Hwy 97 approximately 5
miles north of Redmond Oregon. The
way is well marked so make sure you
look for signs at your turns, the way is
well marked.

Course Yardage & Par:
M-5573 yards, par 72.
W-5354 yards, par 72.

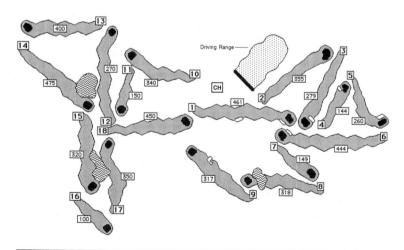

Crosswater (private with reicprocal agreement)
P.O. Box 4818; Sunriver, OR 97707; (503) 593-6191
Pro: to be determined. 18 hole championship course, driving range.
Rating/Slope: the golf course has yet to be rated. **Course record:** N/A.
Greens fee: member only; reciprocates with Sunriver Lodge $95.
Power cart: private club, members only. **Pull cart:** private club, members only.
Trail fee: not allowed. **Reservation policy:** resident member 10 days in advance,
golf member 7 days in advance. **Winter condition:** closed from October to June.
Terrain: flat, some hills. **Tees:** grass. **Temporary greens:** no. **Services:** club
rentals. The course will offer the golfer a full service clubhouse and golf facility.
Comments: this first rate facility is due to open in 1995 and will be nothing short
of spectacular. The course is Heathland style having bentgrass throughout.

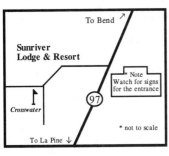

Directions: the golf course is located
approximately 15 miles south of Bend,
Oregon off of Hwy 97 in Sunriver
Oregon. Look for signs to the golf
course. The golf course is not located in
the Sunriver complex.

Course Yardage & Par:
Gold Tees: 7693 yards, par 72.
Silver Tees: 7305 yards, par 72.
Blue Tees: 6842 yards, par 72.
White Tees: 6286 yards, par 72.
Red Tees: 5389 yards, par 72.

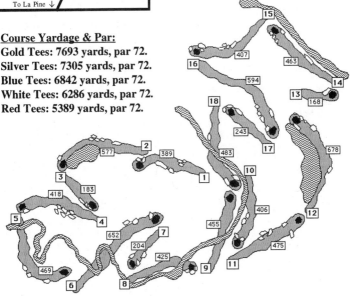

Dutcher Creek Golf Course (public)
4611 Upper River Road; Grants Pass, OR 97526; (503) 474-2188
Manager/Pro: John Kukula. 9 hole course, dual tees for 18 holes.
Rating/Slope: C 71.2/118; M 69.9/114; W 68.6/108. **Course record:** N/A.
Greens fee: $98/$12 everday. **Power cart:** $18/$9. **Pull cart:** $1 per 9 holes.
Trail fee: not available. **Reservation policy:** available call one week in advance.
Winter condition: course is open, damp. **Terrain:** flat, some hills. **Tees:** grass.
Temporary greens: no. **Services:** club rentals, lessons, snack bar, beer, wine, pro
shop, practice green, practice area, driving range. **Comments:** golf course opened
for play in July 1994. In the picturesque Rogue Valley lies Dutcher Creek G.C.
with Mtn. views and a year-round creek. Designed in the Scottish links tradition.

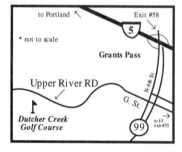

Directions: From I-5 N&S take the
Grants Pass exit and travel toward
downtown Grants Pass. Turn right on
"G" street which turns in to Upper River
Road. Continue on Upper River Road to
the golf course whichwill be on your left
(4 miles from downtown Grants Pass).

Course Yardage & Par:
C-3350 yards, par 36.
M-3135 yards, par 36.
W-2720 yards, par 36.

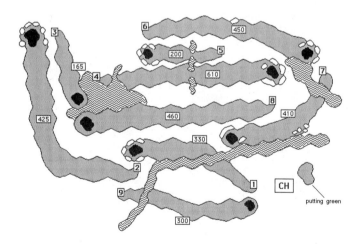

Eagle Creek Golf Course (public)
25805 S.E. Dowty Road; Eagle Creek, OR 97022; (503) 235-4145
Manager: John Bastasch. 9 hole course.
Rating/Slope: the golf course has not been rated yet. **Course record:** 36.
Greens fee: W/D $13/$6.50; W/E $17/$8.50.
Power cart: not available. **Pull cart:** not available. **Trail fee:** N/A.
Reservation policy: yes, you may call anytime. **Winter condition:** open.
Terrain: flat. **Tees:** grass. **Temporary greens:** no.
Services: construction is in progress, limited services at this time.
Comments: Challenging new course with hundreds of mature oak trees.
Water comes into play on several holes. Course will expand to 18 holes in 1996.

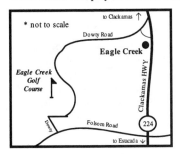

Directions: From Clackamas go southeast to Eagle Creek, Oregon. Travel 1.75 miles to Folsom Road. Turn right and travel 1.1 miles to Dowty Road. Turn right. The golf course is located .5 miles ahead. Look for signs marking your way to the golf course.

Course Yardage & Par:
C-3179 yards, par 35.
M-2878 yards, par 35.
W-1631 yards, par 35.

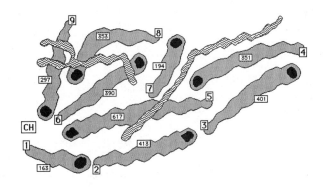

Eagle Crest Resort (public resort)

1522 Cline Falls Road; Redmond, OR 97756; (503) 923-4653
Pro: Terry Anderson, PGA. 18 hole course, driving range.
Rating/Slope: C 71.5/123; M 69.7/121; W 69.8/109. **Course record:** 62.
Greens fee: $37/$22; winter rates; M/C, VISA, AMEX (bankcard guarantee is
required if making more than one tee time). **Power cart:** $25/$16.
Pull cart: $2/$1. **Trail fee:** not allowed. **Reservation policy:** 1 day in advance.
Thursday before weekend. **Winter condition:** open. **Terrain:** flat, some hills.
Tees: grass. **Temporary greens:** no. **Services:** club rentals, lessons, snack bar,
restaurant, lounge, beer, wine, pro shop, lockers, showers, driving range.
Comments: The course is in excellent condition year round. Great facility.

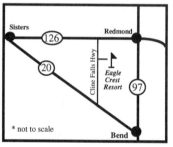

Directions: from Hwy 97 in Redmond
Oregon, travel westbound on Hwy 126
towards Sisters, Oregon. Take the first left
turn which will be Cline Falls Rd., on the
south side of the bridge crossing the
Deschutes River. Travel 1/2 mile to the
resort entrance. **Note:** look for signs to the
entrance of the resort.

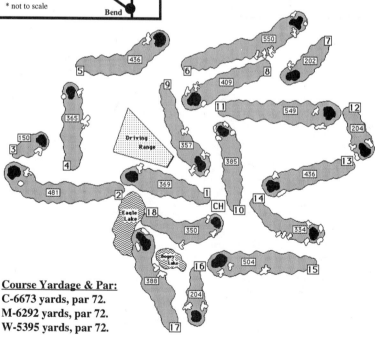

Course Yardage & Par:
C-6673 yards, par 72.
M-6292 yards, par 72.
W-5395 yards, par 72.

Eagle Ridge Golf Course (public resort)

1522 Cline Falls Road; Redmond, OR 97756; (503) 923-5002
Pro: Terry Anderson, PGA. 18 hole course, driving range.
Rating/Slope: C 70.8/123; M 69.0/118; W N/A. **Course record:** N/A.
Greens fee: $37/$22; winter rates; M/C, VISA, AMEX (bankcard guarantee
is required if making more than one tee time). **Power cart:** $25/$16.
Pull cart: $2/$1. **Trail fee:** not allowed. **Reservation policy:** 1 day in advance.
Thursday before weekend. **Winter condition:** open. **Terrain:** flat, some hills.
Tees: grass. **Temporary greens:** no. **Services:** full services are available at the
Eagle Crest Resort. **Comments:** The course is cut out of old growth juniper with
gently rolling terrain. Very challenging course with 69 traps and four lakes.

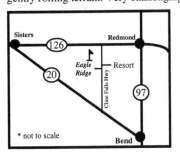

Directions: from Hwy 97 in Redmond
Oregon, travel westbound on Hwy 126
towards Sisters, Oregon. Take the first left
turn which will be Cline Falls Rd., on the
south side of the bridge crossing the
Deschutes River. Travel 1/2 mile to the
resort entrance. Look for signs to the golf
course the way is well marked.

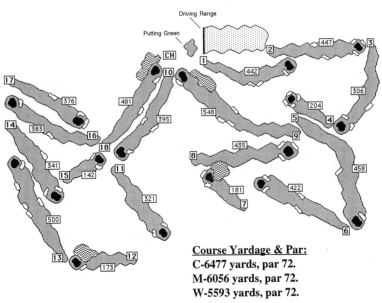

Course Yardage & Par:
C-6477 yards, par 72.
M-6056 yards, par 72.
W-5593 yards, par 72.

Eastmoreland Golf Course (public)

2425 SE Bybee Blvd.; Portland, OR 97202; (503) 292-8570 Tee-Times
Pro: Clark Cumpston, PGA. 18 hole course, range. (503) 775-2900 pro shop.
Rating/Slope: C 71.7/123; M 70.0/119; W 71.4/117. **Course Record**: 63.
Greens fee: W/D $15/$8; W/E $17/$9, non-residents add $2 per nine holes.
Sr. and Jr. rates; no credit cards.**Power cart**: $22/$11. **Pull cart**: $3/$2.
Trail fee: $4/$2. **Reservation policy**: yes, please call 1 week in advance for times.
Winter condition: open all year long. **Terrain**: flat, some hills. **Tees**: grass.
Temporary greens: yes. **Services**: club rentals, lessons, restaurant, beer, wine,
pro shop, driving range.   **Comments**: Scenic golf course rated in the top 25 public
courses in *Golf Digest*. U.S. National Amateur Public Links Championships held
here in 1990. The upgraded clubhouse and well managed pro shop are fantastic.

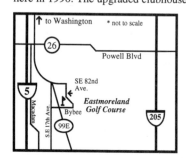

Directions: from I-5 N&S take the The
Dalles/Oregon City exit. Follow signs to
Oregon City onto Mcloughlin Blvd (99E)
southbound. Take the Eastmoreland/Reed
College exit. Turn right onto the overpass
back over Mcloughlin. The clubhouse and
parking lot are located left. Just across the
overpass. Look for signs marking your
way to the golf course.

Course Yardage & Par:
C-6508 yards, par 72.
M-6142 yards, par 72.
W-5646 yards, par 72.

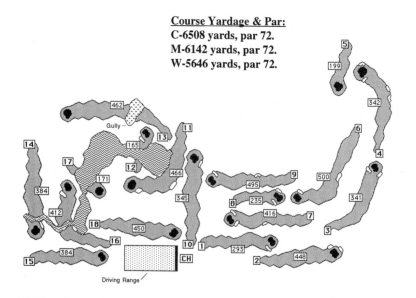

Echo Hills Golf Course (public)

PO Box 187; 100 Golf Course Road; Echo, OR 97826; (503) 376-8244
Manager: Randy Sperr. **9 hole course, dual tees for 18 holes.**
Rating/Slope: M 68.1/113; W 68.8/117. **Course record:** 67.
Greens fee: W/D $12/$6; W/E $16/$8; Sr., Jr. and winter rates; M/C, VISA.
Power cart: $20/$10. **Pull cart:** $2/$1.50 **Trail fee:** $3.
Reservation policy: no. **Winter condition:** open, dry. **Terrain:** very hilly.
Tees: grass. **Temporary greens:** no. **Services:** club rentals, snack bar, beer,
wine, pro shop, driving range. **Comments:** The course is well kept and very
green. Hilly terrain makes this short course a challenge. The terrain will give the
golfer a variety of different lies from the fairway. Excellent golf course

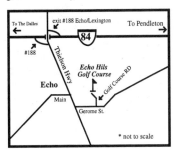

Directions: from I-84 E&W take the
Echo/Lexington exit #188. Proceed for 1
mile to Gerome (Echo Schools). Golf
course entrance will be ahead on your left
hand side. **Note:** look for a sign marking
your entrance to the golf course.

Course Yardage & Par:
M-2884 yards, par 36.
W-2531 yards, par 37.
Dual Tees 18 holes:
M-5867 yards, par 72.
W-5719 yards, par 74.

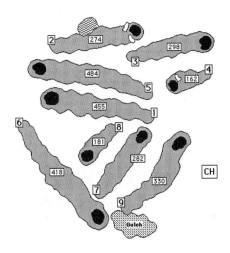

Elkhorn Valley Golf Course (public)

32295 Little North Fork Road; Lyons, OR 97358; (503) 897-3368
Manager: Elizabeth Wolf. 9 hole course, putting green.
Rating/Slope: C 71.4/136; M 68.8/126; W 63.6/108. **Course record:** 67.
Greens fee: $22/$12 all week long; no credit cards.
Power cart: $20/$10. **Pull cart:** $2. **Trail fee:** no charge.
Reservation policy: yes, 1 week in advance. **Winter condition:** golf course
is closed from November 1st to February 28th. **Terrain:** flat, some hills.
Tees: grass. **Temporary greens:** no. **Services:** club rentals, snack bar, beer,
wine, pro shop. **Comments:** Rated by the National Golf Foundation as one
of the best 9 hole golf courses in the United States. Fantastic golf course.
If you are looking for a change of pace in a great setting try Elkhorn Valley.

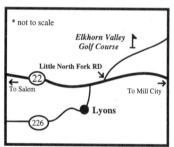

Directions: if you are coming from
Salem travel eastbound on Hwy 22
for approximately 25 miles to Lyons,
Oregon. Turn left on Little North
Fork Road. Proceed for 10 miles to the
golf course. Look for signs on the Hwy
marking your turn to the golf course.

Course Yardage & Par:
Yellow tees: 3169 yards, par 36.
Red tees: 2829 yards, par 36.
Green tees: 2445 yards, par 36.
Blue tees: 2009 yards, par 36.

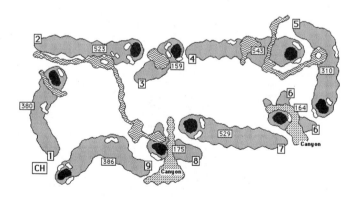

Emerald Valley Golf Club (public)

83293 Dale Kuni Road; Creswell, OR 97426; (503) 895-2174
Head Pro: Mike Coleman. 18 hole course, driving range.
Rating/Slope: C 73.0/126; M 70.8/122; W 74.7/129. **Course record:** 64.
Greens fee: M-Thur. $24/$14; F-Sun. $27/$17; Jr/Sr rates; M/C, VISA, AMEX.
Power cart: $20/$12. **Pull cart:** $3/$2. **Trail fee:** not allowed.
Reservation policy: yes, 1 week in advance. **Winter condition:** open, dry.
Terrain: flat, some hills. **Tees:** grass. **Temporary greens:** N/A.
Services: club rentals, lessons, snack bar, restaurant, lounge, beer, wine, liquor, pro shop, showers, driving range. **Comments:** Beautiful championship course which is in great condition all year round. Excellent greens that are well bunkered and fast during the peak golfing season. This course is worth a trip.

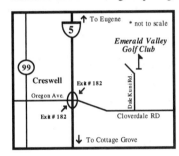

Directions: from I-5 N&S take the Creswell exit #182 and go east for .75 miles to Dale Kuni Rd. Turn north (left) on Dale Kuni Rd and proceed for .5 miles to the golf course. Look for a sign on I-5 marking your exit.

Course Yardage & Par:
C-6873 yards, par 72.
M-6388 yards, par 72.
W-5803 yards, par 73.

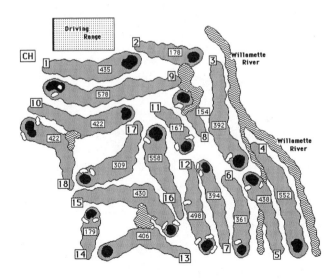

Eugene Country Club (private)

255 Country Club Road; Eugene, OR 97401; (503) 344-5124
Pro: Ron Weber, PGA. 18 hole course, driving range.
Rating/Slope: C 73.9/136; M 71.7/133; W 73.4/135. **Course record:** 66.
Greens fee: private club, members & guests only; reciprocates; no credit cards.
Power cart: private club, members & guests only.
Pull cart: private club, complimentary. **Trail fee:** not allowed.
Reservation policy: yes, 1 day in advance after 10am. **Winter condition:** dry.
Terrain: relatively hilly. **Tees:** grass. **Temporary greens:** no.
Services: full service private country club, driving range. **Comments:** Eugene
Country Club is one of the finest, best kept private golf facilities in the state.

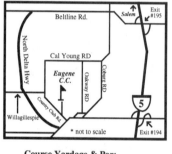

Directions: from I-5 N&S take exit
#195 and head west on Beltline Road.
From Beltline Road take the North Delta
Hwy exit and go southbound. Proceed
to Willagillespie and go east to Country
Club Road and the golf course.

Course Yardage & Par:
C-6837 yards, par 72.
M-6421 yards, par 72.
W-5805 yards, par 72.

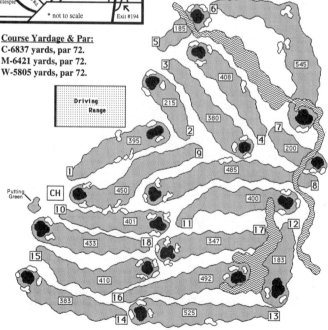

Evergreen Golf Club (public)

11694 W Church Road NE; Mt. Angel, OR 97362; (503) 845-9911
Owners: Joe Druley & Maryann Mills. 9 hole course.
Rating/Slope: M 67.2/109; W 70.8/111. **Course record:** 66.
Greens fee: W/D $19/$10; W/E $20/$11; M/C, VISA.
Power cart: $18/$9. **Pull cart:** $2. **Trail fee:** no charge.
Reservation policy: yes, call ahead for the weekend. **Winter condition:** open.
Terrain: flat, easy walking golf course. **Tees:** grass. **Temporary greens:** no.
Services: club rentals, lessons, restaurant, beer, wine, liquor, pro shop.
Comments: The course is very easy to walk with flat terrain. Water is a factor
on two different holes. Beautiful views of Mt. Hood from several holes. If you are
looking for a course with a friendly atmoshpere try Evergreen.

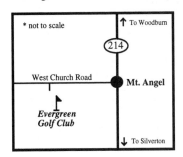

Directions: from Hwy 214 go west
on West Church Road. Follow West
Church Road for 1.1 miles to the
golf course entrance on your left.
Note: Look for the golf course sign
on Hwy 214 that will indicate your turn.

Course Yardage & Par:
M-3034 yards, par 35.
W-3034 yards, par 37.

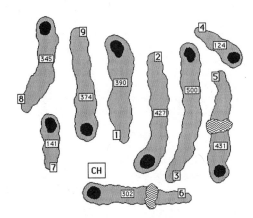

Fiddler's Green Golf Course & Driving Range (public)

91292 Hwy 99 N; Eugene, OR 97402; (503) 689-8464 or (800) 999-6565
Owners: Al, Tim, Matt Whalen. 18 hole par 3 course, lighted driving range.
Rating/Slope: no golf course ratings. **Course record:** 22, 9 holes/44, 18 holes.
Greens fee: $9/$5 all week long; Jr. and Sr. rates; M/C, VISA.
Power cart: not available. **Pull cart:** $1.50. **Trail fee:** not allowed.
Reservation policy: no. **Winter condition:** open, wet from November to March.
Terrain: flat. **Tees:** grass. **Temporary greens:** no. **Services:** club rentals,
lessons, snack bar, beer, wine, huge pro shop, lighted driving range.
Comments: facility has the largest on-course pro shop in the world. Excellent
facility to practice your entire game. Great course for beginners and families.

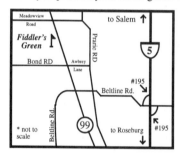

Directions: from I-5 take the Beltline exit
(airport exit) to Hwy 99. You will travel
on Beltline for approximately 5 miles. Go
north on Hwy 99 as if going to the airport.
Continue on Hwy 99 past the airport to the
golf course on your left. If you are north of
Eugene on I-5 you can also take the Halsey
exit. Turn west to Halsey and proceed to the
flashing stop light. Turn south on Hwy 99
through Halsey, Harrisburg and Junction
City. Fiddlers Green is located 4 miles
south of Junction City on the west side
of the Hwy.

Course Yardage & Par:
M-2378 yards, par 54.
W-2378 yards, par 54.

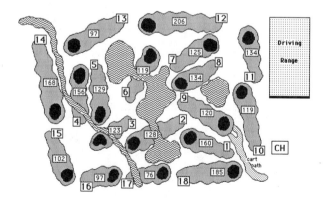

Forest Hills Country Club (semi-private)
#1 Country Club Drive; Reedsport, OR 97467; (503) 271-2626
Pro: Kevin Winston. 9 hole course, dual tees for 18 holes.
Rating/Slope: M 69.8/120; W 71.5/114. **Course record:** 29.
Greens fee: W/D $18/$10; W/E $20/$12; M/C, VISA.
Power cart: $20/$10. **Pull cart:** $3/$2. **Trail fee:** $10.
Reservation policy: yes, during summer & weekends. **Winter condition:** damp.
Terrain: flat, some hills. **Tees:** grass. **Temporary greens:** yes.
Services: club rentals, lessons, restaurant, lounge, beer, wine, liquor, pro shop, driving range. **Comments:** Relatively flat course that is easy to walk. Greens are undulating and can be extremely tough to putt. Well taken care of facility.

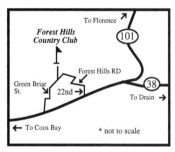

Directions: from Hwy 101 exit west on 22nd St. Turn right on Greenbriar. Turn right on Country Club Dr and proceed to the golf course. **Note:** Look for signs to the golf course marking your way.

Course Yardage & Par:
M-3108 yards, par 36.
W-2774 yards, par 37.
Dual Tees 18 holes:
M-6322 yards, par 72.
W-5548 yards, par 74.

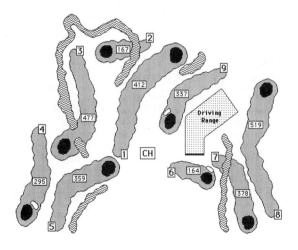

Forest Hills Golf Course (semi-private)
36260 SW Tongue Lane; Cornelius, OR 97113; (503) 357-3347
Pro: Bruce Clark, PGA. Manager: Dick Speros. 18 hole course.
Rating/Slope: M 69.7/122; W 71.7/114. **Course record:** 64.
Greens fee: $24/$12, all week long; M/C, VISA.
Power cart: $20/$10. **Pull cart:** $2/$1. **Trail fee:** $10/$5.
Reservation policy: yes, 1 week in advance for tee times.
Winter condition: open. **Terrain:** flat, some hills. **Tees:** grass.
Temporary greens: no. **Services:** club rentals, lessons, snack bar, lounge,
beer, wine, liquor, pro shop, driving range. **Comments:** One of the most scenic
courses in the state of Oregon. Golf course can play tough at times. Worth a trip.

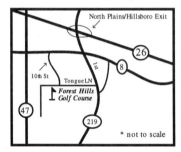

Directions: take Hwy 26 west to the
Hillsboro-North Plains exit. Go Back
across the freeway and follow the road
into Hillsboro. Proceed through Hillsboro
until you are 3 miles south having made
no turns. Turn right on Tongue Lane.
Proceed to the golf course.

Course Yardage & Par:
M-6173 yards, par 72.
W-5673 yards, par 74.

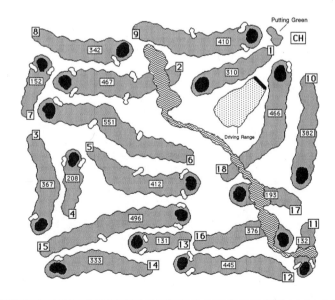

Gearhart Golf Links (public)

N Marion, PO Box 2700; Gearhart, OR 97138; (503) 738-3538
Pro: Jim Smith, PGA. 18 hole course.
Rating/Slope: M 68.5/112; W 72.7/123. Course record: 63.
Greens fee: $25/$13; M/C, VISA. Power cart: $25/$15. Pull cart: $4/$2.
Trail fee: $25/$15. Reservation policy: requested. Winter condition: open, dry.
Terrain: flat, some rolling hills. Tees: grass. Temporary greens: not in use.
Services: club rentals, lessons, snack bar, restaurant, lounge, beer, wine, liquor,
pro shop. Comments: Gearhart Golf Links is the oldest golf course in Oregon or
Washington. Established in 1892 as a 9 hole course, it was extended to 18 holes
in 1913. The greens well bunkered and are always in excellent condition. If you
are looking for a fantastic weekend getaway spot try Gearhart Golf Links.

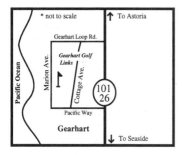

Directions: the golf course is located 1/2
of a mile west of Hwy 101 on the Oregon
coast in Gearhart Oregon. Note: Look for
the sign to the resort and the golf course
from Hwy 101. The path to the golf
course is well marked

Course Yardage & Par:
M-6089 yards, par 72.
W-5882 yards, par 74.

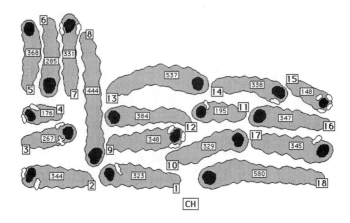

Glendoveer Golf Course (East Course) (public)

14015 NE Glisan St.; Portland, OR 97230; (503) 253-7507, 292-8570 for times
Director of Golf: Daran Dauble, PGA. Head Pro: Jim Chianello.
18 hole course, lighted driving range, putting green, tennis courts.
Rating/Slope: C 69.3/119; M 68.0/116; W 71.2/115. **Course Record:** 62.
Greens fee: W/D $15/$8; W/E $17/$9. **Power Cart:** $22/$11. **Pull Cart:** $2.
Trail fee: $7/$3.50. **Reservation policy:** yes, for weekends only, 6 am to 3pm.
Winter condition: open, dry. **Terrain:** flat, some hills. **Tees:** grass.
Temporary greens: yes. **Services:** club rentals, lessons, snack bar, restaurant,
lounge, beer, wine, liquor, pro shop, lockers, showers, driving range, tennis,
racquetball, jogging trail. **Comments:** golf course is in excellent condition and
is very busy during peak season. The golf course plays fairly tight in spots.

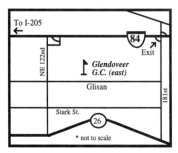

Directions: from I-84 east exit at 181st
NE. Proceed southbound for 1.2 miles to
Glisan Street. Turn westbound for .8 mile
to the golf course. Look for signs.

Course Yardage & Par:
M-6148 yards, par 73.
W-6148 yards, par 77.

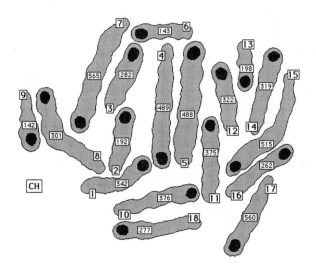

Glendoveer Golf Course (West Course) (public)

14015 NE Glisan St.; Portland, OR 97230; (503) 253-7507, 292-8570 for times
Director of Golf: Daran Dauble, PGA. Head Pro: Jim Chianello.
18 hole course, lighted driving range, putting green, tennis courts.
Rating/Slope: C 67.5/111; M 66.2/109; W 68.2/106. **Course Record**: 62.
Greens fee: W/D $15/$8; W/E $17/$9. Power Cart: $22/$11. Pull Cart: $2.
Trail fee: $7/$3.50. Reservation policy: for weekends only, 6 am to 3pm.
Winter condition: course is open, dry. **Terrain:** flat, some hills. **Tees:** grass.
Temporary greens: yes. **Services:** club rentals, lessons, snack bar, restaurant,
lounge, beer, wine, liquor, pro shop, lockers, showers, driving range, tennis,
racquetball, jogging tail. **Comments:** Course is in excellent condition all year long.
Great driving range at the course location for those wanting to hit a bucket of balls.

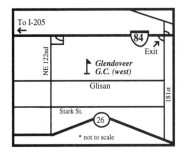

Directions: from I-84 east exit at 181st
NE. Proceed southbound for 1.2 miles to
Glisan Street. Turn westbound for .8 mile
to the golf course. Look for signs.

Course Yardage & Par:
M-5803 yards, par 71.
W-5803 yards, par 75.

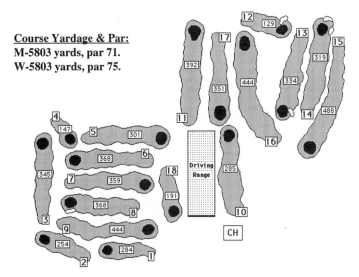

Golf Club of Oregon, The (public)
905 NW Spring Hill Drive; Albany, OR 97321; (503) 928-8338
Manager: Rich Gosser. Pro: Kathy Martin. 18 hole course, driving range.
Rating/Slope: C 68.1/107; M 66.6/107; W 68.5/109. **Course record: 61.**
Greens fee: $20/$11; Jr. and Sr. rates (weekdays only); no credit cards.
Power cart: $20/$10. **Pull cart:** $3/$2. **Trail fee:** $10/$5.
Reservation policy: yes, weekends only. **Winter condition:** open.
Terrain: flat. **Tees:** grass. **Temporary greens:** N/A. **Services:** club rentals,
lessons, snack bar, beer, wine, pro shop, lockers, driving range (irons only).
Comments: The course is easy to walk and has a friendly atmosphere and staff.
The golf course has good drainage and plays well during the winter months.

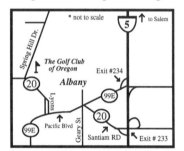

Directions: from I-5 N&S take exit #233
(Satiam Hwy 20) and go westbound to
Main St. and turn right. Proceed to 1st
Avenue and turn left (one way). Proceed
to Lyons and turn right. Go over the bridge
and take your first right on Spring Hill
Drive. Proceed to the golf course on your
right. Look for signs marking your way.

Course Yardage & Par:
C-5773 yards, par 70.
M-5545 yards par 70.
W-5042 yards, par 71.

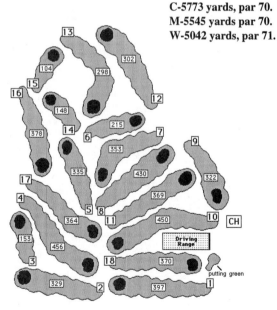

Grants Pass Golf Club (semi-private)
230 Espey Road; Grants Pass, OR 97527; (503) 476-0849
Pro: Ed Fisher, PGA. 18 hole course, driving range.
Rating/Slope: C 71.1/130; M 69.8/128; W 73.5/126. **Course record:** 63.
Greens fee: $30/$18 all week long; M/C, VISA.
Power cart: $20/$12. **Pull cart:** $1. **Trail fee:** not allowed.
Reservation policy: yes, call 2 days in advance. **Winter condition:** open.
Terrain: relatively hilly. **Tees:** grass. **Temporary greens:** no. **Services:** club
rentals, lessons, snack bar, restaurant, lounge, beer, wine, liquor, pro shop, lockers,
showers, driving range. **Comments:** Beautiful layout that winds through trees and
landscaped terrain. Public play is available after members play on a daily basis.

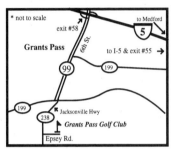

Directions: from I-5 N&S take the Grants Pass exit #55 which will put you on 6th St. Follow accross the river onto Hwy 238. Go south for 3 miles to Espey Road. Turn left to the golf course. The golf course is located approximately 6 miles from the freeway. Look for signs marking your way the way is well indicated.

<u>**Course Yardage & Par:**</u>
C-6367 yards, par 72; M-6077 yards, par 72; W-5687 yards, par 73.

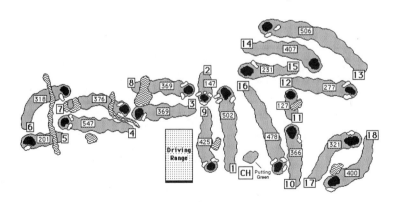

Greenlea Golf Course (public)
26736 SE Kelso Road; Boring, OR 97009; (503) 663-3934
Owners: Walt & Muriel Markham. 9 hole executive course.
Rating/Slope: the golf course is not rated. **Course record:** 26.
Greens fee: W/D $9/$4.50; W/E $10/$5; no credit cards.
Power cart: power carts are not available. **Pull cart:** $2. **Trail fee:** no charge.
Reservation policy: none. **Winter condition:** closed from December 1st to
February. **Terrain:** flat, some hills. **Tees:** grass. **Temporary greens:** no.
Services: club rentals, small pro shop, vending machines, putting green.
Comments: two sets of tees are available for a full 18 hole round of golf. The
golf course is flat and very easy to walk. Great course for seniors and beginers.

Directions: from Hwy 212 trun right
on Richey Road which will become SE
Kelso Road. The golf course is located
approximately 1.3 miles ahead on your
left hand side. The golf course is located
1.5 miles south of Boring, Oregon.

Course Yardage & Par:
M-1510 yards, par 30.
W-1510 yards, par 30.

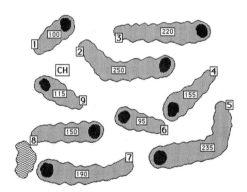

Gresham Golf Course (semi-private)
2155 NE Division; Gresham, OR 97030; (503) 665-3352
Pro: Stuart Smart, PGA. 18 hole course, driving range.
Rating/Slope: M 67.3/105; W 69.0/107. **Course record:** 62.
Greens fee: W/D $16/$9*; W/E $19/$11.50*; Jr. rates; M/C, VISA.
Power cart: $23/$14*. **Pull cart:** $2*. **Trail fee:** N/A. (*subject to change).
Reservation policy: yes, for weekends only (advised). **Winter condition:** open.
Terrain: flat, some hills. **Tees:** grass. **Temporary greens:** no.
Services: club rentals, lessons, restaurant, lounge, beer, wine, liquor, pro shop,
driving range. **Comments:** The course is in excellent condition all year round.
The staff is friendly and helpful. Excellent walking golf course for seniors.

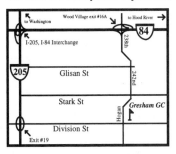

Directions: from I-205 take the Division
St exit. Proceed eastbound for 8 miles to
the golf course. From I-84 take Wood
Village exit and go south. Proceed to
Division and turn left to the golf course.
The golf course is located 1 block ahead
on your left hand side.

Course Yardage & Par:
M-5814 yards, par 72.
W-5284 yards, par 72.

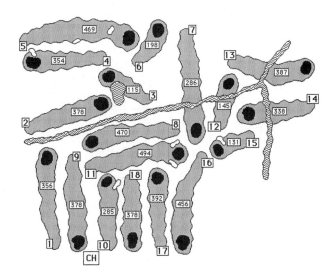

Harbor Links Golf Course (public)

601 Harbor Isles Boulevard; Klamath Falls, OR 97601; (503) 882-0609
Pro: Rocky Warner, PGA. 18 hole course, driving range.
Rating/Slope: C 69.3/117; M 68.5/115; W 71.2/119. **Course record:** 63.
Greens fee: W/D $20/$12; W/E & Holidays $23/$15; winter rates; M/C, VISA.
Power cart: $20/$12. **Pull cart:** $4/$3. **Trail fee:** not allowed.
Reservation policy: yes, call a day ahead. **Winter condition:** wet. **Terrain:** flat.
Tees: grass. **Temporary greens:** no. **Services:** club rentals, lessons,
snack bar, restaurant, lounge, beer, wine, liquor, pro shop, driving range.
Comments: Located on Klamath Lake. A links type course with many water
hazards. Good golf course that can play very tough. Worth a trip if in the area.

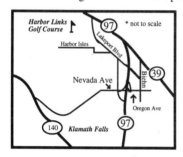

Directions: from Hwy 97 exit at Nevada
Ave and head westbound. Turn right at
Montelus St. Continue ahead to Lakeport
Blvd and turn left. Proceed to Habor Isles
Blvd and the golf course. The golf course
is located on Klamath Lake.

Course Yardage & Par:
C-6268 yards, par 72.
M-6076 yards, par 72.
W-5709 yards, par 72.

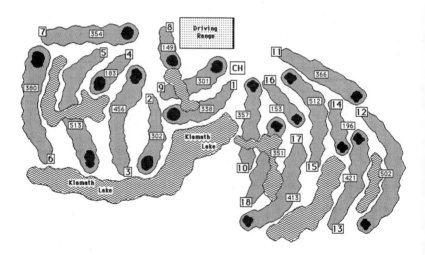

Hawk Creek Golf Course (public)

PO Box 497 (off Hwy 101); Neskowin, OR 97149; (503) 392-4120
Owners: Darin & Judy Galle. 9 hole course.
Rating/Slope: M 63.8/103; W N/A. **Course record:** 29.
Greens fee: $17/$9 all week long; M/C, VISA.
Power cart: $17/$9. **Pull cart:** $2/$1. **Trail fee:** $3.
Reservation policy: yes, reservations are taken for tee times in the summer.
Winter condition: the course is open all year, weather permitting. **Terrain:** flat, some hills, very walkable. **Tees:** grass. **Temporary greens:** not in use.
Services: club rentals, snack bar, very small pro shop, beer, wine, putting green.
Comments: the golf course is beautifully situated in a valley minutes from the scenic Oregon Coast. Great golf course if you want to play a quick nine holes.

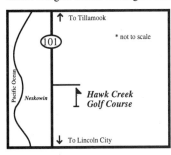

Directions: the golf course is located on the east side of Hwy 101 at Neskowin. Look for a black & white sign from Hwy 101 marking the entrance to the golf course. Your turn is well marked.

Course Yardage & Par:
M-2343 yards, par 34.
W-2343 yards, par 36.

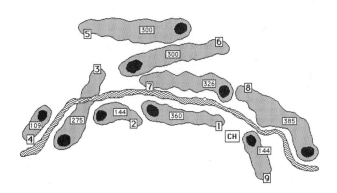

Heron Lakes Golf Club; Great Blue Course (public)
3500 N Victory Blvd.; Portland, OR 97217; (503) 289-1818, 292-8570 for times
Pro: Byron Wood, PGA. 18 hole course. Course record: N/A.
Rating/Slope: T 73.6/132; C 71.3/128; M 69.4/122; W 69.8/120.
Greens fee: $20/$12 all week long; no credit cards.
Power cart: $22. **Pull cart:** $3/$2. **Trail fee:** $4/$2.
Reservation policy: yes, 1 week in advance. **Winter condition:** open.
Terrain: flat. **Tees:** grass. **Temporary greens:** no.
Services: club rentals, lessons, snack bar, beer, pro shop, driving range.
Comments: Great Blue is one of the toughest public courses in the northwest
but definitely the best buy. This golf course alone is worth a special trip. The golf
course has several bunkers and lakes that come into play on almost every hole.

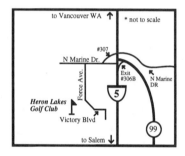

Directions: from I-5 take exit #306B
(West Delta Park/Portland International
Raceway). From the north swing sharply
to the right off exit ramp to the intersection with N. Victory Blvd. Proceed
straight to N. Broadacres Rd. Turn left
on N. Broadacres (which becomes N.
Broadacre St). Turn right at intersection
of N. Force Ave and follow this to the
golf course entrance. From the south,
turn left onto N. Victory Blvd off the
freeway exit, then right (north) at "T" to
N. Broadacres Rd. Follow same as above
from this point.

Heron Lakes Golf Club; Greenback Course (public)
3500 N Victory Blvd.; Portland, OR 97217; (503) 289-1818, 292-8570 for times
Pro: Byron Wood, PGA. 18 hole course. Course record: 66.
Rating/Slope: C 71.4/124; M 68.4/115; W 69.4/113.
Greens fee: W/D $12/$6.50; W/E $14/$7.50; Jr. & Sr. rates; no credit cards.
Power cart: $22. **Pull cart:** $3/$2. **Trail fee:** $4/$2.
Reservation policy: yes, 1 week in advance. **Winter condition:** open.
Terrain: flat. **Tees:** grass. **Temporary greens:** no.
Services: club rentals, lessons, snack bar, beer, pro shop, driving range.
Comments: Course has some of the nicest greens in Oregon. You will find the
course in excellent condition throughout the entire year. The course also has a
driving range for those who want to practice before or after the round.

Course Yardage & Par:
(Great Blue Course)
T-6916 yards, par 72.
C-6504 yards, par 72.
M-6056 yards, par 72.
W-5285 yards, par 72.

Course Yardage & Par:
(Greenback Course)
C-6595 yards, par 72.
M-5938 yards, par 72.
W-5224 yards, par 72.

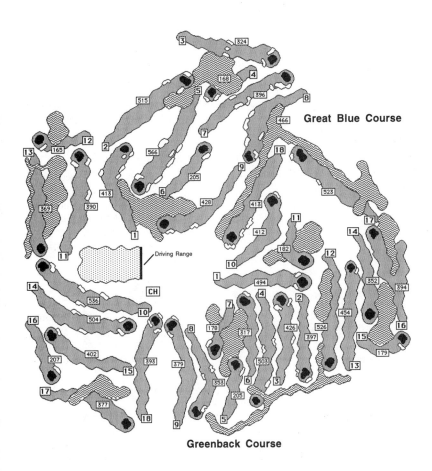

Great Blue Course

Driving Range

Greenback Course

Hidden Valley Golf Course (public)
775 N River Road; Cottage Grove, OR 97424; (503) 942-3046
Pro: none. 9 hole course, dual tees for 18 holes.
Rating/Slope: M 67.0/113; W 68.4/114. **Course record:** 57 (18 holes).
Greens fee: $16/$10*; Jr. rates; M/C, VISA. (* subject to change).
Power cart: $18/$12*. **Pull cart:** $3/$2*. **Trail fee:** $10/$6*.
Reservation policy: yes, taken on the weekends. **Winter condition:** wet, with
good drainage. **Terrain:** flat, some hills. **Tees:** grass. **Temporary greens:** no.
Services: club rentals, lessons, restaurant, lounge, beer, wine, liquor,
pro shop, lockers. **Comments:** Large trees and small greens make shot
placement important on this course. Great golf course for a quick 9 holes.

Directions: from I-5 southbound take
the first Cottage Grove exit (second exit
if going northbound, #174) and proceed
west for 1/2 mile. Veer left at Pacific
Highway. Turn right on Woodson. Turn
right to the golf course. Look for signs.

Course Yardage & Par:
M-2774 yards, par 35.
W-2448 yards, par 36.
Dual tees 18 holes:
M-5635 yards, par 70.
W-4970 yards, par 72.

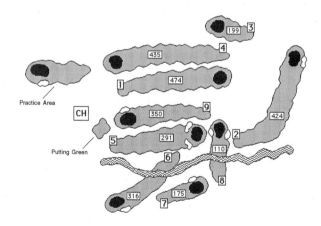

The Highlands at Gearhart (public)
#1 Highlands Road; Gearhart, OR 97138; (503) 738-5248
Pro: Dan Strite, PGA. 9 hole executive course.
Rating/Slope: M 59/94; W N/A. **Course Record: 25.**
Greens fee: $15/$8; winter rates; M/C, VISA.
Power Cart: $15/$10. **Pull Cart:** $1. **Trail fee:** not allowed
Reservation policy: summer, up to 7 days in advance. **Winter condition:** open.
Terrain: flat, some hills. **Tees:** grass. **Temporary greens:** N/A.
Services: club rentals, pro shop with large inventory, snack bar, lessons.
Comments: This challenging 9 hole course is set in a beautiful ocean view
setting. Hole #5 is the signature hole where a cliff comes into play. Great course.

Directions: golf course is located 1 mile
north of Gearhart, Oregon off of Highway
101. Take Del Rey Beach access off of
Highway 101. Travel westbound for 1/4
mile to the golf course. Look for signs
that are posted on the highway.

Course Yardage & Par:
Yellow Nine: M-1776 yards, par 31.
W-1776 yards, par 34.
Blue Nine: M-1761 yards, par 31.
W-1761 yards, par 33.
White Nine: M-1618 yards, par 31.
W-1618 yards, par 34.

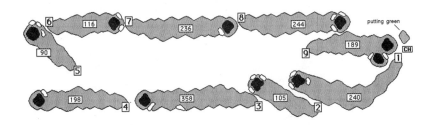

Hood River Golf & Country Club (public)

1850 Country Club Road; Hood River, OR 97031; (503) 386-3009
Pro: Dave Waller, PGA. 9 hole course, dual tees for 18 holes.
Rating/Slope: M 67.6/111; W 68.4/104. **Course record:** 64.
Greens fee: W/D $15/$8; W/E $17/$9; Jr. & Sr. rates available; M/C, VISA.
Power cart: $15/$8. **Pull cart:** $2. **Trail fee:** $3.
Reservation policy: yes, call up to 1 week in advance for tee times.
Winter condition: closed when snow covered only. **Terrain:** relatively hilly.
Tees: grass. **Temporary greens:** no. **Services:** club rentals, lessons,
snack bar, restaurant, lounge, beer, wine, liquor, pro shop, driving range.
Comments: Beautiful setting with view of Mt. Hood and Mt. Adams.

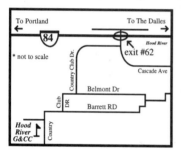

Directions: from I-84 E&W take exit #62.
Go south and take Country Club Road for
2.2 miles. At stop, where road "Y,s" turn
right. The golf course is located 1.1 miles
ahead on your right hand side.

Course Yardage & Par:
M-2920 yards, par 36.
W-2695 yards, par 37.
Dual tees 18 holes:
M-5605 yards, par 72.
W-5246 yards, par 74.

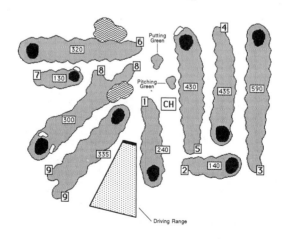

Illahe Hills Country Club (private)
3376 Country Club Drive; Salem, OR 97302; (503) 581-3233
Pro: Gary L. Dowen, PGA. 18 hole course, driving range.
Rating/Slope: C 72.7/129; M 71.0/126; W 72.3/122. **Course Record:** 64.
Greens fee: private members only; no credit cards. **Power Cart:** private club.
Pull Cart: complimentary. **Trail fee:** not allowed. **Reservation policy:** yes, 2
days in advance. **Winter condition:** open, damp. **Terrain:** flat, some hills.
Tees: grass. **Temporary greens:** no. **Services:** club rentals, lessons, snack bar,
restaurant, lounge, beer, wine, liquor, pro shop, lockers, showers, driving range.
Comments: course has been host to several tournaments, including the 1981
U.S.G.A. Junior Girls National Championship. Great, tough golf course.

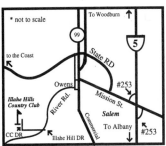

Directions: from I-5 N&S take the
Mission exit and go westbound. Turn left
on Commercial. At Owens, turn right.
Follow Owens as it veers south and
changes to River Road. Follow for 3.7
miles to the golf course. The golf course
is located on the west side of the city.

Course Yardage & Par:
C-6722 yards, par 72.
M-6401 yards, par 72.
W-5598 yards, par 73.

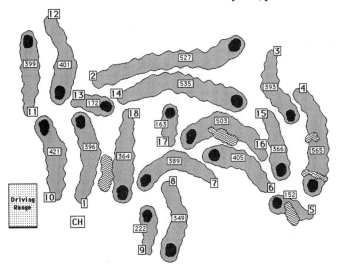

Illinois Valley Golf Club (public)

Laurel Road, PO Box 924; Cave Junction, OR 97523; (503) 592-3151
Pro: Rex Denham, PGA. 9 hole course, dual tees for 18 holes.
Rating/Slope: M 69.1/117; W 71.1/120. **Course Record:** 65.
Greens fee: $18/$10; Jr & Sr rates; twilight rates.
Power Cart: $18/$10. **Pull Cart:** $2/$1. **Trail fee:** not allowed.
Reservation policy: yes, necessary for weekends and holidays.
Winter condition: open, dry. **Terrain:** flat. **Tees:** grass.
Temporary greens: no. **Services:** club rentals, lessons, snack bar, beer,
wine, pro shop, driving range, putting green. **Comments:** course has two sets of
tees for those who want to play a full 18 holes. Excellent well kept golf course.

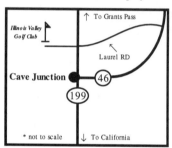

Directions: the golf course is located
1/2 mile north of the city of Cave Junction
off of Hwy 199. The golf course will be
located on your west side of the Hwy.

Course Yardage & Par:
M-3049 yards, par 36.
W-2731 yards, par 36.
Dual tees 18 holes:
M-6029 yards, par 72.
W-5358 yards, par 72.

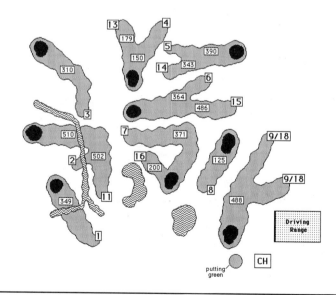

Indian Creek Golf Course (public)
3605 Brookside Drive; Hood River, OR 97031; (503) 386-7770
Pro: Treve Gray, PGA. 18 hole course, driving range.
Rating/Slope: C 70.0/126; M 67.4/118; W 67.7/116. **Course record:** 67.
Greens fee: W/D $20/$11; W/E $24/$12; Sr. & Jr rates, Sr. rates M-W all day.
Power cart: $20/$10. **Pull cart:** $2. **Trail fee:** $5.
Reservation policy: yes, taken up to 2 weeks in advance, tournaments anytime.
Winter condition: open, weather permitting. **Terrain:** flat, rolling terrain.
Tees: grass. **Temporary greens:** no. **Services:** club rentals, lessons, pro shop,
driving range. **Comments:** the course provides excellent drainage for winter
play. The golf course is fairly easy to walk with gentle rolling hills. Great views.

Directions: from I-84 E&W take exit #62
and turn right. Follow Cascade St into
town. Turn right on 13th St and proceed
approximately 1.2 miles to Brookside Dr.
Turn right to the golf course which is .8
miles ahead. Look for signs along the way.

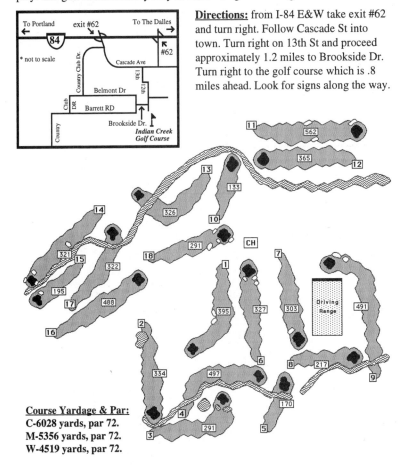

Course Yardage & Par:
C-6028 yards, par 72.
M-5356 yards, par 72.
W-4519 yards, par 72.

Jim Colbert's Hound Hollow Golf Center & DR (public)

23010 West Arata Road; Wood Village, OR 97060; (503) 669-2290
Pro: Dode Forrester, PGA; 9 hole course; covered, lighted driving range.
Rating/Slope: the golf course has not been rated. **Course record:** 26.
Greens fee: W/D $8; W/E $10; Jr/Sr, winter rates; M/C, VISA. **Trail fee:** N/A.
Power cart: $11. **Pull cart:** $2. **Reservation policy:** yes and recommended.
Winter condition: open. **Terrain:** flat. **Tees:** grass. **Temporary greens:** no.
Services: pro shop, snack bar, driving range, 18 hole putting course, lessons,
club rentals, beer, wine. **Comments:** course is owned by Senior PGA pro Jim
Colbert. A unique feature is a miniature 18 hole all-grass putting green that is
fully lighted for nighttime use. The 9 hole course is a very challenging layout.

Directions: from I-84 head eastbound and
exit at Wood Village. From your exit
proceed southbound on NE 238th Dr. until
you reach W Arata Road. Turn right on W
Arata Road and proceed to the golf course.
Note: Watch for signs from the Hwy
marking your way to the golf course. The
golf course is adjacent to Multnomah
Greyhound Park.

Course Yardage & Par:
M-1511 yards, par 30.

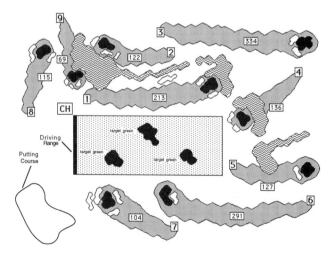

John Day Golf Club (semi-private)

W Hwy 26, PO Box 176; John Day, OR 97845; (503) 575-0170
Manager: Bev Pierson. 9 hole course, dual tees for 18 holes.
Rating/Slope: M 67.2/104; W 71.2/111. **Course record:** 62.
Greens fee: $18/$12; VISA; the clubhouse is private.
Power cart: $18/$10. **Pull cart:** $1. **Trail fee:** $5.
Reservation policy: no. **Winter condition:** closed Mondays in winter.
Terrain: flat, some hills. **Tees:** grass. **Temporary greens:** N/A.
Services: snack bar, beer, wine, liquor, pro shop, lockers, driving range.
Comments: course has two sets of tees to allow you to play a full 18 holes.
Trees and water can be a factor when playing this golf course.

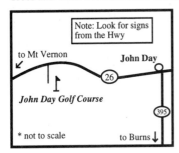

Directions: the golf course is located 3 miles west of John Day Oregon on Hwy 26. Make sure you look for a sign on the Hwy to the golf course location.

Course Yardage & Par:
M-2955 yards, par 36.
W-2896 yards, par 38.
Dual tees 18 holes:
M-5942 yards, par 71.
W-5618 yards, par 75.

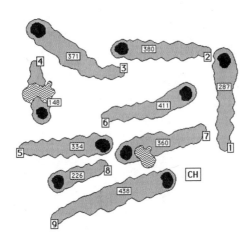

Juniper Golf Club (semi-private)

139 SE Sisters Avenue; Redmond, OR 97756; (503) 548-3121
Pro: Bruce Wattenburger, PGA. 18 hole course, driving range.
Rating/Slope: C 71.3/124; M 69.8/120; W 70.9/115. **Course record:** 65.
Greens fee: W/D $20/$12; W/E $25/$15; Jr. and winter rates; M/C, VISA.
Power cart: $20/$11. **Pull cart:** $2/$1. **Trail fee:** $7.50 daily.
Reservation policy: yes, 1 month in advance. **Winter condition:** open.
Terrain: flat, some hills. **Tees:** grass. **Temporary greens:** not in use.
Services: club rentals, lessons, snack bar, restaurant, beer, wine, liquor,
pro shop, lockers, showers, driving range. **Comments:** This beautiful golf
course wanders through Juniper trees and lava rock. Great golf course.

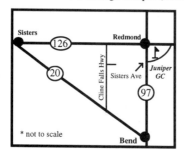

Directions: golf course located 1/4 mile off of Hwy 97 at the south end of Redmond Oregon. Proceed east on Sisters Avenue for 1/4 mile to the golf course. Course located next to the Redmond City Airport. Look for signs.

Course Yardage & Par:
C-6525 yards, par 72.
M-6211 yards, par 72.
W-5598 yards, par 72.

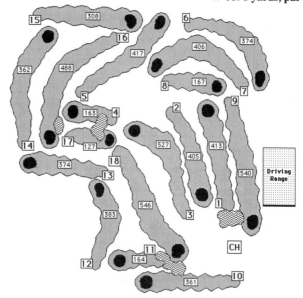

KAH-NEE-TA Resort Course (public)

PO Box K, 100 Main Street; Warm Springs, OR 97761
(503) 553-1112 or (800) 831-0100. Pro: Mark Visintainer. 18 hole course.
Rating/Slope: C 73.1/123; M 69.7/118; W 70.0/116. **Course record: 59.**
Greens fee: $30/$18; Jr./Sr.; winter rates; M/C, VISA, DIN, AMEX, DIS.
Power cart: $22/$12. **Pull cart:** $2. **Trail fee:** $7.
Reservation policy: yes, call 2 weeks in advance. **Winter condition:** open, dry.
Terrain: flat. **Tees:** grass. **Temporary greens:** no. **Services:** club rentals,
lessons, snack bar, restaurant, lounge, beer, wine, liquor, pro shop, driving range.
Comments: The pro states this is where the birdies fly and eagles soar in over
300 days of sunshine a year. Excellent facility. Great vacation spot for the family.

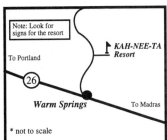

Directions: course is located 120 miles
southeast of Portland on Hwy 26. Follow
the signs to the resort. Golf course is
located 11 miles north of Warm Springs
Oregon. Follow the signs to the resort.

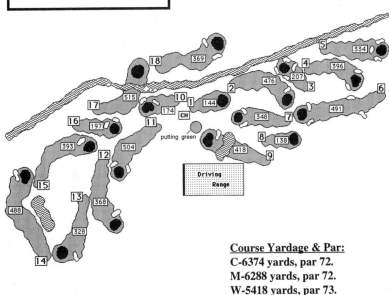

Course Yardage & Par:
C-6374 yards, par 72.
M-6288 yards, par 72.
W-5418 yards, par 73.

Kentuck Golf Course (public)
680 Golf Course Lane; North Bend, OR 97459; (503) 756-4464
Pro: Martin Culp. 18 hole course, putting green.
Rating/Slope: M 65.5/99; W 69.8/107. **Course record:** 62.
Greens fee: W/D $12/$7; W/E $14/$8; Jr. rates; M/C, VISA, DIS.
Power cart: $15/$8. **Pull cart:** $1. **Trail fee:** $5.
Reservation policy: yes, please call ahead for a tee time.
Winter condition: open, dry. **Terrain:** flat. **Tees:** grass.
Temporary greens: yes. **Services:** club rentals, lessons, snack bar, pro shop,
beer, wine. **Comments:** Course setting is beautiful and has a challenge for any
level of golfer. Creeks, ponds come into play on nearly every hole.

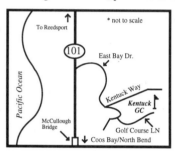

Directions: golf course located northeast
of North Bend Oregon. Go east on East
Bay Dr at the north end of the McCull-
ough Bridge (where Hwy 101 crosses
Coos Bay and Kentuck inlet). Follow the
road to the southeast. Proceed for 3 miles
to the golf course. Look for signs marking
your way to the golf course.

Course Yardage & Par:
M-5394 yards, par 70.
W-4469 yards, par 70.

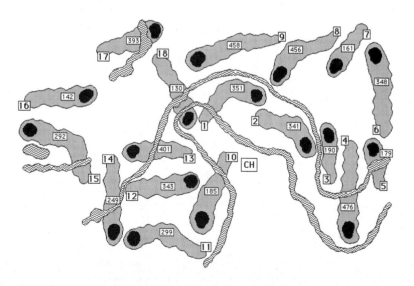

Killarney West Golf Club (public)

1275 NW 334th; Hillsboro, OR 97124; (503) 648-7634
Owner: J. E. O'Meara. 9 hole course.
Rating/Slope: M 64.4/108. **Course record**: 32.
Greens fee: W/D $12/$6; W/E $16/$8; no credit cards.
Power cart: $14/$7. **Pull cart:** $1. **Trail fee:** $7/$3.50.
Reservation policy: yes, taken for weekends and holidays.
Winter condition: open, dry. **Terrain:** flat, some hills. **Tees:** grass.
Temporary greens: no. **Services:** club rentals, snack bar, beer, wine,
small pro shop. **Comments:** Course is very scenic with large trees and green
surroundings. Water is a factor on several holes throughout the golf course.

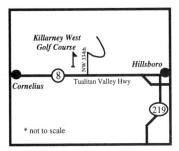

Directions: golf course is located
between Cornelius and Hillsboro Oregon
off of Hwy 8. Proceed northbound on NW
334th for 1/2 mile to the golf course.

Course Yardage & Par:
M-2544 yards, par 36.
W-2544 yards, par 37.

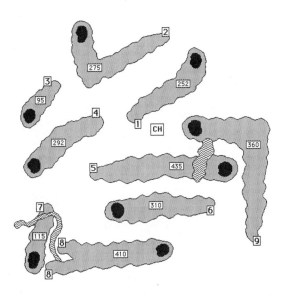

75

King City Golf Course (semi-private)

15355 SW Royalty Parkway; King City, OR 97224; (503) 639-7986
Pro: Bob Gasper, PGA. **9 hole course.**
Rating/Slope: M 61.9/90; W 64.6/96. **Course record: 59.**
Greens fee: W/D$18/$9; W/E $20/$10; no credit cards.
Power cart: $20/$10. **Pull cart:** $2. **Trail fee:** not allowed.
Reservation policy: yes, call for reservations during the summer season.
Winter condition: wet. **Terrain:** flat. **Tees:** grass. **Temporary greens:** no.
Services: club rentals, pro shop, lockers, showers.
Comments: the golf course is an excellent par 33 tract. The course is very easy
to walk with very few hazards to contend with. Worth a trip if in the area.

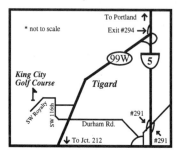

Directions: from I-5 N&S take exit for
Hwy 99W #294 (west Pacific Hwy).
Travel south to King City. When in King
City turn right on Durham Rd. Proceed to
SW 116th and go north then take the first
left to SW Royalty and proceed ahead to
the golf course. Look for signs that are
posted along the way. The route is well
marked.

Course Yardage & Par:
M-2428 yards, par 33/34.
W-2337 yards, par 35.

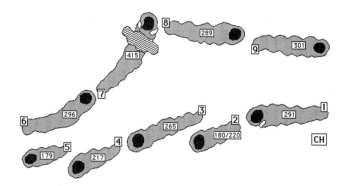

Kinzua Hills Golf Club (semi-private)
Off of Hwy 19; Fossil, OR 97830; no phone
Pro: none. 6 hole course.
Rating/Slope: M 58.3/92; W 61.3/97. **Course record:** 20.
Greens fee: $8 all day; no credit cards.
Power cart: none. **Pull cart:** none. **Trail fee:** not allowed.
Reservation policy: none. **Winter condition:** closed during bad weather.
Terrain: flat, some hills. **Tees:** grass. **Temporary greens:** no.
Services: the golf course has very limited services.
Comments: The only 6 hole golf course in Oregon. Each hole has 3
sets of tees for 18 hole play. Course often payed for on the honor system.

Directions: the golf course is located off
Hwy 19 in Fossil, Oregon. From Hwy 19
go eastbound toward Kinzua. While in
Kinzua on Hwy 19 travel northbound to
the golf course.

Course Yardage & Par:
M-1463 yards, par 22.
W-1388 yards, par 24.
(the par for 9 holes is 32).

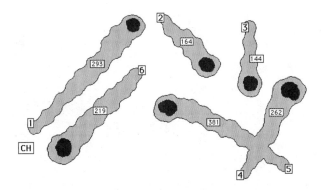

The Knolls Golf Course (public)

1919 Recreation Lane; Sutherlin, OR 97479; (503) 459-4422
Pro: Mike Deprez. 18 hole course, driving range. (*subject to change)
Rating/Slope: C 70.3/121; M 69.2/119; W 71.5/122. **Course record: 64.**
Greens fee: W/D $16/$10*; W/E $18/$10*; winter; Sr. rates Fri. only; M/C, VISA.
Power cart: $18/$9. **Pull cart:** $2/$1. **Trail fee:** $3/$2. **Reservation policy:** yes,
1 week in advance. **Winter condition:** open. **Terrain:** flat with rolling hills.
Tees: grass. **Temporary greens:** no. **Services:** club rentals, lessons, snack bar,
restaurant, lounge, beer, wine, pro shop, driving range, nightly entertainment.
Comments: course has had extensive upgrades to provide an outstanding golfing
experience. Tree lined fairways alternates with open links style design. RV Parking
is available for those wanting to spend the night. Friendly, well kept public course.

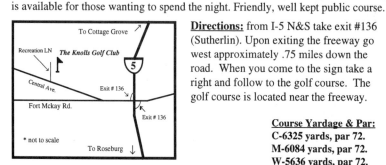

Directions: from I-5 N&S take exit #136
(Sutherlin). Upon exiting the freeway go
west approximately .75 miles down the
road. When you come to the sign take a
right and follow to the golf course. The
golf course is located near the freeway.

Course Yardage & Par:
C-6325 yards, par 72.
M-6084 yards, par 72.
W-5636 yards, par 72.

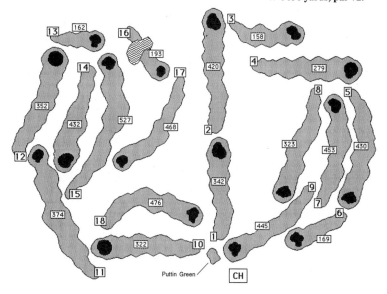

La Grande Country Club (private)

10605 S McAlister Road, PO Box 836; Island City, OR 97850; (503) 963-4241
Pro: Bill Rosholt, PGA. 9 hole course, dual tees for 18 holes.
Rating/Slope: M 69.9/121; W 70.9/120. **Course record: 63.**
Greens fee: private club members & guests only; reciprocates.
Power cart: private club. **Pull cart:** private club. **Trail fee:** $7.
Reservation policy: yes, 1 week in advance. **Winter condition:** open, weather
permitting.   **Terrain:** flat, some hills. **Tees:** grass. **Temporary greens:** no, tees.
Services: club rentals, lessons, lounge, beer, wine, pro shop, driving range.
Comments: Long narrow course built amidst an apple orchard. Postage stamp
greens make this lush golf course a challenge for any level of golfer.

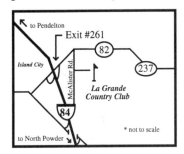

Directions: from I-84 take the Hwy 82
exit in Island City. Proceed east for 2
miles then turn right on McAllister to the
golf course which is 2 blocks ahead on
your left hand side. Look for a sign
marking your turn to the clubhouse.

Course Yardage & Par:
M-3267 yards, par 36.
W-2849 yards, par 38.
Dual tees 18 holes:
M-6514 yards, par 72.
W-5653 yards, par 75.

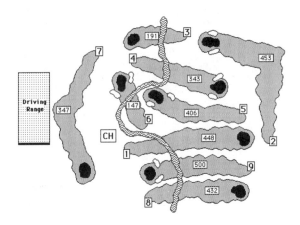

Lake Oswego Golf Course (public)

17525 SW Stafford Road; Lake Oswego, OR 97034; (503) 636-8228
Pros: Chris Smith, Patty Miller. Manager: Cindy Lincoln.
18 hole executive course, driving range, putting green.
Rating/Slope: the golf course is not rated. **Course Record:** 51.
Greens fee: W/D $11/$6; W/E $12/$7; Jr. & Sr. rates (weekdays only).
Power cart: $6, dry season only. **Pull cart:** $2. **Trail fee:** N/A.
Reservation policy: Monday thru Thursday first come first serve. Friday thru
Sunday make reservations 7 days in advance. **Winter condition:** open, damp.
Terrain: flat, some hills. **Tees:** grass. **Temporary greens:** yes, in winter.
Services: club rentals, lessons, snack bar, driving range. **Comments:** golf course
is great for seniors and those who want to practice their short game. Driving range
is partially covered for use during inclement weather. Good executive track.

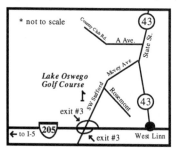

Directions: from I-205 exit (#3) at SW
Stafford. Proceed for 2.5 miles northbound on SW Stafford. The golf course
will be located on your left hand side.
You can also reach the golf course by
taking Highway 43. Look for signs.

Course Yardage & Par:
M-2724 yards, par 61.
W-2724 yards, par 67.

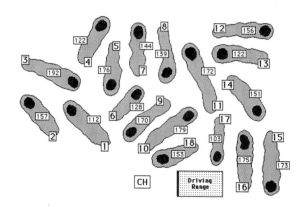

Lakeridge Golf & Country Club (semi-private)

Highway 140 W; HC 60, Box 199; Lakeview, OR 97630; (503) 947-3855
Owners: Ed & Diane Almojuela. 9 hole course, dual tees for 18 holes.
Rating/Slope: M 70.0/119; W 71.6/121. **Course record**: 65.
Greens fee: $14/$9 all week long; Jr. rates; M/C, VISA.
Power cart: $15/$9. **Pull cart**: $2. **Trail fee**: $8/$4.
Reservation policy: no. **Winter condition**: closed from January to March 31st.
Terrain: flat. **Tees**: grass. **Temporary greens**: no. **Services**: club rentals,
lessons, snack bar, restaurant, beer, wine, pro shop, lockers, driving range.
Comments: This picturesque course is surrounded by the Warner Mountains
and the Fremont National Forest. Golf course is in excellent condition.

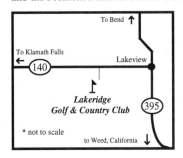

Directions: the golf course is located 3
miles west of Lakeview off Hwy 140.
From Klamath Falls travel 90 miles east
on Hwy 140 to the golf course. Look for
signs marking your way to the golf course.

Course Yardage & Par:
M-3323 yards, par 36.
W-2965 yards, par 37.
Dual tees 18 holes:
M-6647 yards, par 72.
W-5863 yards, par 74.

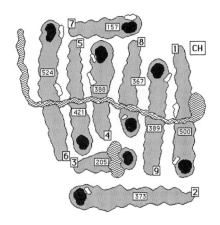

Lakeside Golf & Racquet Club (public)

3245 Club House Drive; Lincoln City, OR 97367; (503) 994-8442
Pro: Rudy Frykberg, PGA. 18 hole course, driving range.
Rating/Slope: M 64.9/109; W 66.2/104. **Course record: 60.**
Greens fee: $25/$15*; Sr. rates; M/C, VISA. (*subject to change).
Power cart: $25/$15*. **Pull cart:** $2*. **Trail fee:** available.
Reservation policy: yes, please call ahead for tee times. **Winter condition:** open.
Terrain: relatively hilly, but walkable. **Tees:** grass. **Temporary greens:** no.
Services: club rentals, lessons, snack bar, beer, wine, pro shop, lockers,
showers, driving range (irons only). **Comments:** golf course is in good condition.
At this golf course you will find rolling fairways and excellent greens.

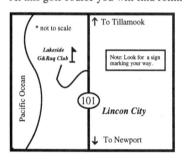

Directions: the golf course is located on
the west side of Hwy 101 at the north
end of Lincoln City. Look for a sign
marking the entrance to the course.

Course Yardage & Par:
C-5006 yards, par 66.
M-4689 yards, par 66.
W-4318 yards, par 71.

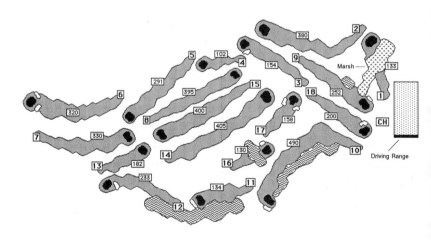

Langdon Farms Golf Club (public)

24377 NE Airport Road; Aurora, OR 97002; (503) 678-GOLF (4653)
Dir. of Golf: Julius Aquino. 18 hole course, practice range, putting course.
Rating/Slope: the golf course has not been rated. **Course record:** N/A.
Green fees: W/D $45; W/E $50; M/C, VISA.
Power cart: $20/$12. **Pull cart:** $4. **Trail fee:** not available.
Reservation policy: yes, please call up to 30 days in advance for tee times.
Winter condition: open. **Terrain:** relatively hilly, with depressed fairways.
Tees: grass. **Temporary greens:** no. **Services:** club rentals, lessons, snack bar,
bar cart, lounge, restaurant, lockers, showers, pro shop, practice range, putting
course (bentgrass). **Comments:** course is to open in May of 1995. The facility is
going to be one of the finest new public courses to hit the golf scene in the greater
Portland area in a long time. "State of the art" practice range boast's the largest
grass teeing surface in the Northwest. Fantastic new golf course.

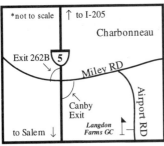

Directions: from I-5 take exit #282B.
Travel eastbound then turn right on NE
Airport Road. Travel 1 mile to the main
entrance. Look for signs marking your
turn to the entrance of the facility.

Course Yardage & Par:
T-6911 yards, par 71.
C-6577 yards, par 71.
M-6088 yards, par 71.
W-5283 yards, par 71.

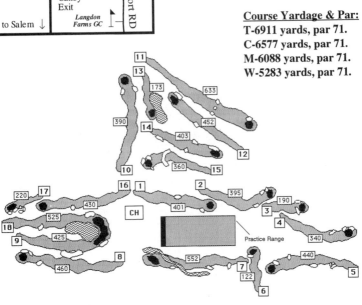

Laurel Hill Golf Course (public)

9450 Old Stage Road, PO Box 167; Gold Hill, OR 97525; (503) 855-7965.
Managers: Jan & Peter Fish. 9 hole executive course.
Rating/Slope: the golf course is not rated. **Course record:** 27.
Greens fee: W/D $9/$5; W/E $11/$6; Jr. & Sr. rates; M/C, VISA.
Power cart: none. **Pull cart:** $1. **Trail fee:** no charge.
Reservation policy: yes, call ahead of time, recommended on the weekends.
Winter condition: open, damp to dry. **Terrain:** flat, some hills.
Tees: grass, mats in winter. **Temporary greens:** no. **Services:** club rentals,
lessons, snack bar, beer, wine, pro shop, driving range. **Comments:** A challenging irons course of great scenic beauty, but not intimidating for beginners.

Directions: from I-5 N&S take exit #40 (Gold Hill/Jacksonville). Travel east for .25 miles on Old Stage Road to the golf course. The golf course will be located on your left hand side. Look for signs marking your turn to the parking lot.

Course Yardage & Par:
M-1915 yards, par 31.
W-1915 yards, par 31.

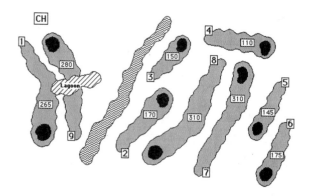

Laurelwood Golf Course (public)

2700 Columbia Avenue; Eugene, OR 97403; (503) 687-5321, 484-4653
Pros: Joe Rauchenburg, Mike Booth. 9 hole course, driving range.
Rating/Slope: C 69.5/129; M 68.1/125; W 70.4/124. **Course record:** 59.
Greens fee: W/D $12/$7; W/E $13/$8; Jr. & Sr. rates; M/C, VISA.
Power cart: $17/$9. **Pull cart:** $3/$2. **Trail fee:** $4 (9 holes).
Reservation policy: yes, please call ahead, especially in the summer months.
Winter condition: open. **Terrain:** relatively hilly. **Tees:** grass. **Services:** club
rentals, lessons, sandwiches, beer, juices, pro shop, covered driving range, wedding
receptions. **Comments:** The golf course is in excellent condition after significant
changes last year. Lots of hills for interesting shot making and exercise.

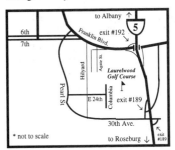

Directions: I-5 northbound take 30th Ave
exit to Hilyard. Turn right on Hilyard to E
24th turn right on E 24th. Proceed to
Columbia and take a right. Proceed to the
top of the hill. The pro shop is on the
lower level. From I-5 southbound take the
Eugene/University exit. Follow signs to
the University of Oregon (Franklin Blvd
to Agate St). Turn right on Agate St to E
24th. Proceed to Columbia and turn right.

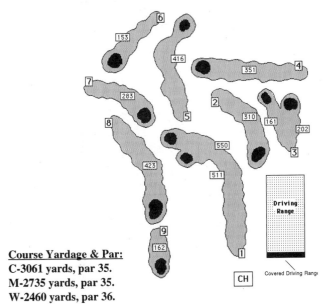

Course Yardage & Par:
C-3061 yards, par 35.
M-2735 yards, par 35.
W-2460 yards, par 36.

Lone Pine Village Golf (public)

355 Lone Pine Drive; The Dalles, OR 97058; (503) 298-2800
Manager: Bill Blackburn. Pro: Steve Welker. 9 hole course, driving range.
Rating/Slope: to be determined. **Course record:** to be determined.
Greens fee: to be determined upon opening of the golf course.
Power cart: to be determined. **Pull cart:** to be determined. **Trail fee:** N/A.
Reservation policy: to be determined upon opening. **Winter condition:** open.
Terrain: flat. **Tees:** grass. **Temporary greens:** no. **Services:** club rentals, snack
bar, lessons, lounge, restaurant, beer, wine, liquor, pro shop, driving range, putting
green, motel, RV park. **Comments:** golf course is now in the early construction
stages. Full service driving range is now open to serve you.

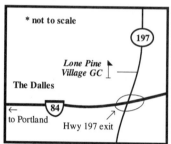

Directions: from I-84 E&W exit at the
junction for Hwy 197. Turn northbound
off the exit. The golf course and the driving
range will be immediately on your left hand
side. Look for a sign posting your turn into
the complex.

Course Yardage & Par:
(Yardage & Par are tentative)
M-2500 yards, par 32.
W-2500 yards, par 32.

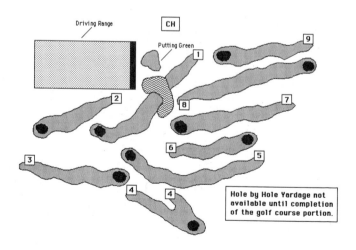

Manzanita Golf Course (public)
PO Box 21; Lakeview Drive; Manzanita, OR 97130; (503) 368-5744
Owners: Steve and Penny Erickson. 9 hole course.
Rating/Slope: M 61.8/97; W 63.2/102. **Course record:** 29.
Greens fee: $22/$11 all week long; no credit cards.
Power cart: none. **Pull cart:** $1 (per 9 holes). **Trail fee:** not allowed.
Reservation policy: yes, taken and recommended. **Winter condition:** open.
Terrain: flat, some hills. **Tees:** grass. **Temporary greens:** no.
Services: club rentals, snack bar, pro shop, driving range, putting green.
Comments: Picturesque course located on the beautiful Oregon coast. This course is worth a trip if you are driving the Oregon coast and want to play a quick 9 holes.

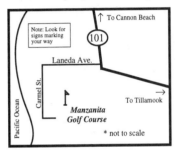

Directions: from Hwy 101 N&S take Manzanita Junction exit toward the beach. You will be on Laneda Ave. Follow Laneda for .6 miles to S Carmel Ave (there is a sign to the golf course) turn left. Go through residential area for .8 miles to the golf course on your left. The golf course is located at the intersection of Lakeview Dr and NeCarney Blvd.

Course Yardage & Par:
M-2192 yards, par 32; W-2100 yards, par 33.

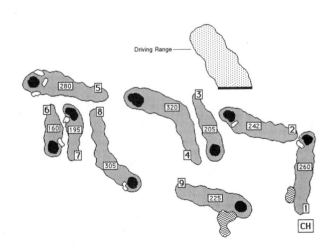

Marysville Golf Course (public)

2020 SW Allen Street: PO Box 1203; Corvallis, OR 97339; (503) 753-3421
Owner: R. M. Hoselton. 9 hole course, putting green.
Rating/Slope: M 69.8/no slope; W 75.8/no slope. **Course record**: 31.
Greens fee: W/D $13/$8; W/E $14/$9; annual memberships; no credit cards.
Power cart: none available. **Pull cart:** $2. **Trail fee:** no charge.
Reservation policy: call in advance for tee time policy. **Winter condition:** dry.
Terrain: flat, walkable course. **Tees:** grass. **Temporary greens:** no.
Services: club rentals, beer, wine, small pro shop, practice area, putting green.
Comments: Family owned golf facility that is well kept and offers a great family
golfing atmosphere. The golf course is fairly wide open with only a few hazards.

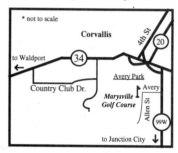

Directions: from Hwy 20, take Avery
Park exit. When entering the park, take
left-hand fork in entry road. Go Through
park. At stop sign at park's edge, go
straight to course. From I-5 go west on
Hwy 34 into Corvallis, onto Harrison to
4th Ave and proceed down to Avery and
turn right. Go to Allen and turn to the golf
course.

Course Yardage & Par:
M-3296 yards, par 36.
W-2909 yards, par 39.

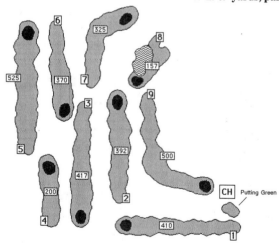

McKenzie River Golf Course (public)
PO Box 98; Walterville, OR 97489; (503) 896-3454
Owners: Rod & Diane Omlid, Ivan & Sally Holte.
9 hole course. Rating/Slope: M 66.7/103; W 71.2/116. **Course record: 29.**
Greens fee: W/D$17/$10; W/E $18/$10; Jr. rates weekdays only; no credit cards.
Power cart: $18/$9. **Pull cart:** $1.50. **Trail fee:** no trail fee.
Reservation policy: yes, 1 day in advance. **Winter condition:** open, dry.
Terrain: flat. **Tees:** grass. **Temporary greens:** yes. **Services:** club rentals, snack bar, beer, pro shop. **Comments:** course has a 10 hole punch card for your green fees at $75. The electric carts are available for those who really need them. Course is in excellent condition all year long. Beautiful mountain setting.

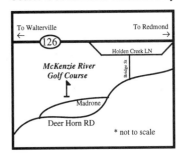

Directions: from Hwy 126 exit at Holden Creek Lane. Follow past mile post 17 to Bridge Street which crosses the river. Turn on Madrone which leads you right to the clubhouse.

Course Yardage & Par:
M-2800 yards, par 35.
W-2272 yards, par 35.
(*note: par is 71 for 18 holes)

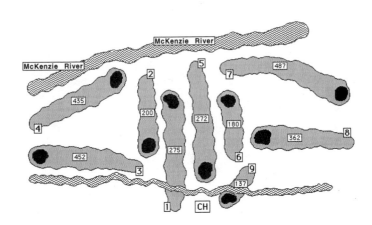

McNary Golf Club (semi-private)
6255 River Road N; Keizer, OR 97303; (503) 393-4653
Pro: Rich Brown, PGA. 18 hole course, putting green.
Rating/Slope: C 69.3/117; M 68.2/114; W 71.2/116. **Course record:** 62.
Greens fee: W/D $25/$13; W/E $28/$15; Sr. rates; M/C, VISA.
Power cart: $20/$11. **Pull cart:** $2. **Trail fee:** not allowed.
Reservation policy: yes, 1 week in advance. **Winter condition:** open, damp.
Terrain: flat, easy walking golf course. **Tees:** grass. **Temporary greens:** no.
Services: club rentals, lessons, snack bar, restaurant, lounge, beer, wine, liquor,
pro shop, lockers, showers. **Comments:** the golf course offers wide, open
fairways with large greens. The facility is well taken care of. Great golf course.

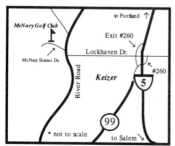

Directions: from I-5 N&S take exit #260
(Lockhaven) and go west on Lockhaven
proceed for 1.3 miles to River Road, turn
right and proceed to McNary Estates Dr.
and turn left to the golf course. Look for
signs marking your entrance to the course.

Course Yardage & Par:
C-6094 yards, par 71.
M-5872 yards, par 71.
W-5535 yards, par 71.

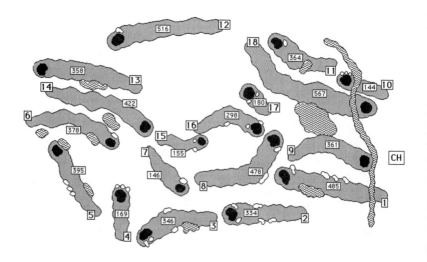

Meadow Lakes Golf Course (public)
300 Meadow Lakes Drive; Prineville, OR 97754; (503) 447-7113
Pro: David Cahill, PGA. 18 hole course, driving range.
Rating/Slope: T 73.1/131; C 71.8/128; M 69.1/121 W 69.0/121. **Record:** 69.
Greens fee: W/D $27/$15; W/E $29/$15 winter rates. **Power cart:** $22/$12.
Pull cart: $3/$2. **Trail fee:** N/A. **Reservation policy:** yes, call ahead for tee times.
Winter condition: open, weather permitting. **Terrain:** beautifully mounded.
Tees: grass. **Temporary greens:** no. **Services:** fully stocked pro shop,
club rentals, lessons, lounge, restaurant, snack bar, liquor, driving range.
Comments: A beautiful new course worth a special trip. Ten ponds, 16 surface
acres of water, 2000 trees, and 66 bunkers will challenge your skill. Great course.

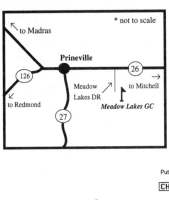

Directions: from Portland take Hwy 26
through Madras to Prineville. In Prineville
the highway becomes 3rd street. Meadow
Lakes Drive will be on your right. There
will be signs to mark your way to the golf
course. From Redmond take Hwy 126 to
Prineville and the course.

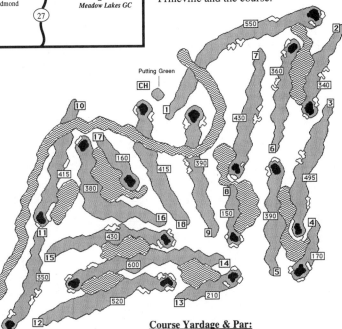

Course Yardage & Par:
T-6731 yards, par 72.   M-5849 yards, par 72.
C-6398 yards, par 72.   W-5155 yards, par 72.

Meadowlawn Golf Club (public)

3898 Meadowlawn Loop SE; Salem, OR 97303; (503) 363-7391
Pro: Greg Ganson, PGA. 9 hole course.
Rating/Slope: M 58.5/92; W 60.5/98. **Course record:** 26.
Greens fee: $18/$9 all week long; M/C, VISA.
Power cart: not available. **Pull cart:** $1.50. **Trail fee:** $9/$5.
Reservation policy: yes, 1 day in advance. **Winter condition:** open.
Terrain: flat, easy walking course. **Tees:** grass. **Temporary greens:** no.
Services: club rentals, lessons, pro shop. **Comments:** The course has rolling
hills and is very easy to walk. The golf course is very tight in places, putting an
emphasis on shot placement. This Salem golf course is a senior favorite.

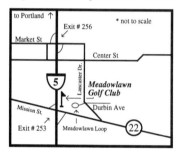

Directions: from I-5 exit #256 (Market
St-Silverton). East on Market St for .6 mi
to Lancaster Dr. Turn right on Lancaster.
Proceed 1.9 mi to Durbin then take a
right, then immediate right on Meadowlawn Loop SE which curves around to
the course on your left. Or take exit #253
and go east on Mission to the first exit you
come to and go north on Lancaster.
Proceed to Durbin and turn left to Meadowlawn Loop Road and to the course.

Course Yardage & Par:
M-2090 yards, par 32.
W-2090 yards, par 34.

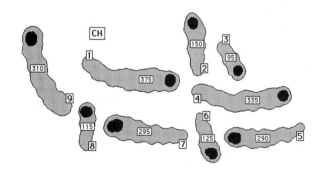

Meriwether National Golf Club (public)

5200 SW Roodbridge Road; Hillsboro, OR 97123; (503) 648-4143
Pro: Jim Petersen, PGA. 27 hole course, natural grass driving range.
Rating/Slope: North/West C 71.3/121; M 69.5/118; W 72.3/113. **Record:** 64.
Greens fee: W/D $16/$9; W/E $20/$11; Jr./monthly Sr. rates; no credit cards
Power cart: $18/$10. **Pull cart:** $2. **Trail fee:** $10/$5.50.
Reservation policy: yes for weekends and holidays. **Winter condition:** dry.
Terrain: flat. **Tees:** grass. **Temporary greens:** no. **Services:** clubhouse with
banquet facilities, club rentals, lessons, snack bar, pro shop, driving range.
Comments: course is very challenging, and includes one of the toughest par 4's
in the state. In additon to the existing 27 holes. Meriwether has plans for another 9
holes, an 18 hole putting green and a covered driving range. All should be in place
by spring of 1996. If you get a chance be sure to try Meriwether National.

Directions: the golf is located at the west
edge of Hillsboro, Oregon. From Hwy 8,
proceed eastbound to River Road. Turn
south on River Road. Turn right on Roodbridge Road and follow this to the course.
Look for signs marking your way to the
golf course. The way is well marked.

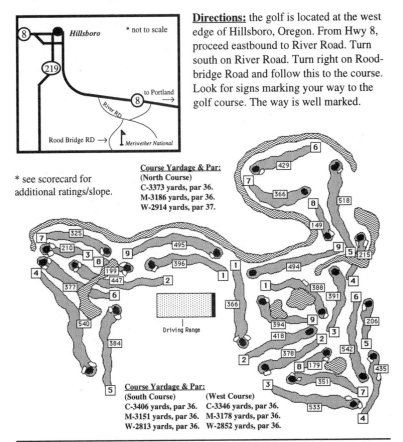

* see scorecard for
additional ratings/slope.

Course Yardage & Par:
(North Course)
C-3373 yards, par 36.
M-3186 yards, par 36.
W-2914 yards, par 37.

Driving Range

Course Yardage & Par:
(South Course)   (West Course)
C-3406 yards, par 36.   C-3346 yards, par 36.
M-3151 yards, par 36.   M-3178 yards, par 36.
W-2813 yards, par 36.   W-2852 yards, par 36.

Michelbook Country Club (private)

1301 Michelbook Lane; McMinnville, OR 97128; (503) 472-8079
Pro: Mel Chaufty, PGA. 18 hole course, driving range.
Rating/Slope: C 71.0/124; M 69.0/127; W 72.0/122. **Course record:** 65.
Greens fee: private club, members & guests only, reciprocates .
Power cart: private club. **Pull cart:** private club. **Trail fee:** private club.
Reservation policy: private club members only. **Winter condition:** open, dry.
Terrain: flat. **Tees:** grass. **Temporary greens:** yes. **Services:** club rentals,
lessons, snack bar, restaurant, beer, wine, lounge, pro shop, driving range.
Comments: lakes, bunkers and tree lined fairways put and emphasis on
shot making. Excellent golf course. The golf course can be very tight in places.

Directions: from Hwy 99 (Pacific Hwy
W). Follow Hwy 99 into town and make
a right turn onto 12th Ave. Proceed to
Michelbook Lane and the golf course.
From Hwy 18 (River Hwy) come into
town and go north on Baker St. and then
take a left on 12th Ave. to the golf course.

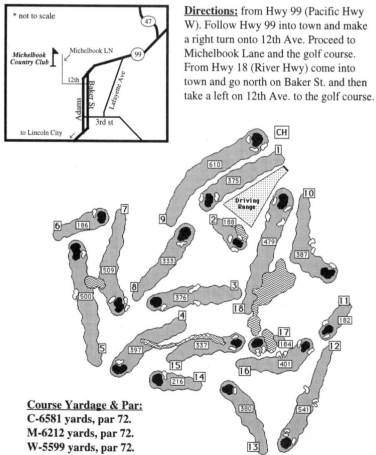

Course Yardage & Par:
C-6581 yards, par 72.
M-6212 yards, par 72.
W-5599 yards, par 72.

Middlefield Village Golf Course & Driving Range (public)

91 Village Drive; Cottage Grove, OR 97424; (503) 942-8730
Head Pro: Tom Deluca. 18 hole course, driving range.
Rating/Slope: M 63.7/104; W 63.4/102. **Course Record:** 64.
Greens fee: W/D $18/$11; W/E $20/$13; Jr. & Sr., college rates.
Power cart: $20/$12. **Pull cart:** $3/$2. **Trail fee:** not allowed. **Reservation**
policy: yes, Saturdays, Sundays & Hol. accepted the preceeding Tues., weekdays
24 hours in advance. **Winter condition:** open, damp. **Terrain:** flat. **Tees:** grass.
Temporary greens: no. **Services:** club rentals, lessons, snack bar, beer, wine,
pro shop, covered driving range, changing room. **Comments:** excellent newer
course. Great learning center and practice facility. Worth a trip if in the area.

Directions: from I-5 north and south in
Cottage Grove take exit # 174. Proceed to
Middlefield Village and the golf facility.

Course Yardage & Par:
M-4908 yards, par 67.
W-4260 yards, par 67.

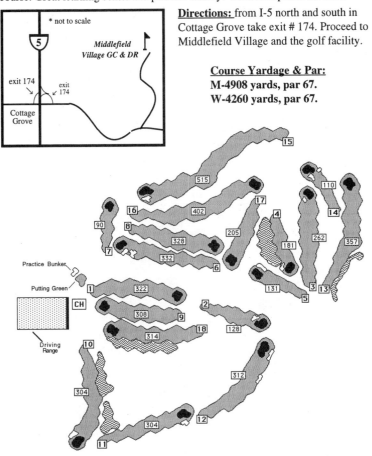

Milton-Freewater Golf Course (public)

W 301 Catherine Street; Milton-Freewater, OR 97862; (503) 938-7284
Pro/Manager: G.R. Gillette. 18 hole executive course.
Rating/Slope: M 55.4/80; W 58.1/83. **Course record:** 54.
Greens fee: W/D $9/$6; W/E $10/$7; Jr. & Sr. rates; no credit cards.
Power cart: $18/$12. **Pull cart:** $1. **Trail fee:** $3.
Reservation policy: yes, for weekends, holidays. **Winter condition:** open, dry.
Terrain: flat, back nine is relatively hilly. **Tees:** grass. **Temporary greens:** no.
Services: club rentals, lessons, restaurant, lounge, pro shop, putting green.
Comments: the golf course is tight in places and is perfect to help you improve
your iron play. Water comes into play on several holes. Good public golf course.

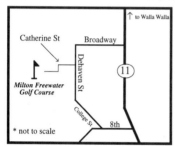

Directions: golf course located in Milton-
Freewater behind high school, west on
Hwy 11. Look for sign on highway for the
turn to the golf course. When in Milton-
Freewater turn westbound on 2nd NW for
.2 miles. Turn right on Dehaven Street.
Proceed to Catherine Street and turn left.

Course Yardage & Par:
M-3346 yards, par 60.
W-3314 yards, par 61.

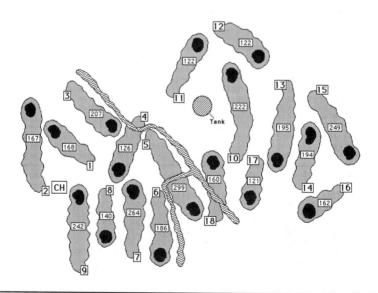

Mountain High Golf Course (public)
60650 China Hat Road; Bend, OR 97862; (503) 382-1111
Pro: Tom Blair, PGA. Manager: Kris Rees. 18 hole course, driving range.
Rating/Slope: C 71.4/126; M 68.9/119; W 71.8/126. **Course record:** 69.
Greens fee: $36/$20*. Credit cards are accepted. (*subject to change).
Power cart: $24/$12*. **Pull cart:** $3/$2*. **Trail fee:** not allowed.
Reservation policy: yes, call 7 days in advance. **Winter condition:** closed from
November 1st to April 1st. **Terrain:** flat. **Tees:** grass. **Temporary greens:** no.
Services: club rentals, pro shop, snack bar, beer, wine, lessons, driving range.
Comments: Fantastic island green on hole #5. Water will come into play on over
half the golf course. Out of bounds everywhere puts a real emphasis on accuracy.

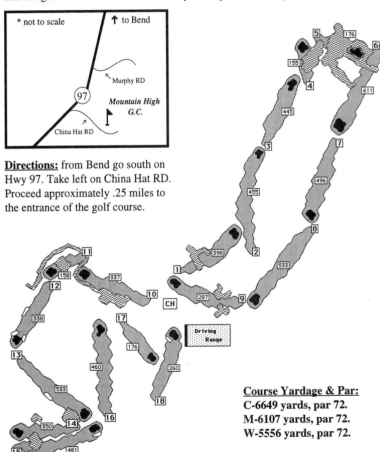

Directions: from Bend go south on
Hwy 97. Take left on China Hat RD.
Proceed approximately .25 miles to
the entrance of the golf course.

Course Yardage & Par:
C-6649 yards, par 72.
M-6107 yards, par 72.
W-5556 yards, par 72.

Mountain View Golf Course (public)

27195 SE Kelso Road; Boring, OR 97009; (503) 663-4869
Pro: Toby Tommaso. **18 hole course, driving range.**
Rating/Slope: C 69.2/122; M 67.6/117; W 69.2/111. **Course record:** 61.
Greens fee: W/D $17/$9.50; W/E $20/$11; Jr. & Sr. rates; M/C, VISA.
Power cart: W/D $20/$11; W/E $22/$12. **Pull cart:** $2.
Trail fee: 1/2 of power cart rental. **Reservation policy:** yes, 1week in advance.
Winter condition: open, weather permitting. **Terrain:** flat, some small hills.
Tees: grass. **Temporary greens:** no. **Services:** club rentals, lessons, snack bar,
restaurant, lounge, beer, wine, liquor, pro shop, driving range. **Comments:** this
course offers beautiful mtn. views and some of the driest winter play in the area.

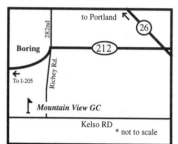

Directions: from Hwy 26 turn west at
flashing yellow light in Boring, proceed 3
miles to the course on your right. You can
also exit at Boring Rd (212) and go west
to Richey Road. Turn left and proceed to
Kelso Road and turn right to the course.

Course Yardage & Par:
C-6041 yards, par 71.
M-5572 yards, par 71.
W-5348 yards, par 73.

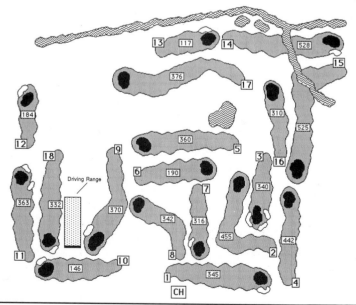

Neskowin Beach Golf Course (public)

Hawk Creek Avenue; PO Box 839; Neskowin, OR 97149; (503) 392-3377
Pro: William W. Martin, PGA. 9 hole course.
Rating/Slope: M 65.3/103; W 67.7/110. **Course record: 28.**
Greens fee: $19/$10; Jr. and Sr. rates (seasonal); no credit cards.
Power cart: $20/$10. **Pull cart:** $2.50/$1.50. **Trail fee:** $3.
Reservation policy: yes, recommended but not required (a must in summer).
Winter condition: closed from November 1st to March 15th. **Terrain:** flat.
Tees: grass & mats. **Temporary greens:** no. **Services:** club rentals, lessons, snack
bar, beer, wine, pro shop, lesson area. **Comments:** Fabulous, well kept turf which
is always green. Small greens and creeks make this golf course a real challenge.

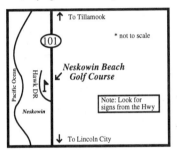

Directions: from Hwy 101, turn north
on Hawk Avenue. The golf course is
located 1/4 mile ahead on your right
hand side. Look for a sign on Hwy 101
marking your turn to the golf course.

Course Yardage & Par:
M-2616 yards, par 35.
W-2516 yards, par 35.

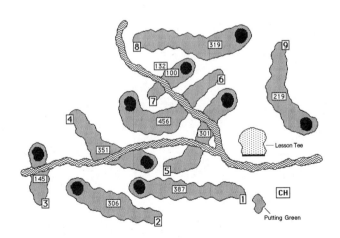

Nine Peaks Golf Course (public)
1152 NW Golf Course Road; Madras, OR 97741; (503) 475-3511
Owners: Kevin & Deirdre O'Meara. 18 hole course.
Rating/Slope: M 67.8/103; W 70.0/107. **Course record: 61.**
Greens fee: W/D $15/$9*; W/E $17/$10*; no credit cards. (*prices will change).
Power cart: $16/$8*. **Pull cart:** $1*. **Trail fee:** $6*. **Reservation policy:** none.
Winter condition: open, however closed periodically due to snow.
Terrain: flat. **Tees:** grass. **Temporary greens:** no. **Services:** lessons, snack bar,
beer, wine, pro shop. **Comments:** The course very flat and is easy to walk. New
nine has several challenging greens guarded by water. Excellent views of the
Cascade Mountain Range. This course is worth a special trip if in Central Oregon.

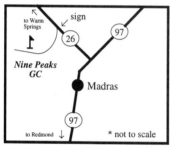

Directions: the golf course is located
off of highway 26, 1 mile west of
Madras, Oregon. Look for the signs on
highway 26 marking your turn to the
golf course. The location of your turn
is well marked.

Course Yardage & Par:
C-6582 yards, par 72.
M-6280 yards, par 72.
W-5745 yards, par 72.

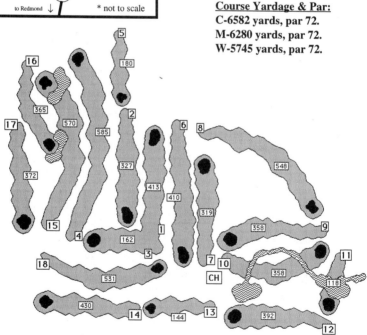

Oak Knoll Public Golf Course (public)
3070 Hwy 66; Ashland, OR 97520; (503) 482-4311
Pro: Bob Haney. 9 hole course, dual tees for 18 holes.
Rating/Slope: M 69.1/119; W 70.5/116. **Course record:** 62.
Greens fee: W/D $12.50/$8.50; W/E $13.50/$9.50; Jr. rates; M/C, VISA.
Power cart: $17/$11. **Pull cart:** $2/$1. **Trail fee:** $6.
Reservation policy: yes, call ahead. **Winter condition:** open, dry. **Terrain:** flat, some hills. **Tees:** grass. **Temporary greens:** no. **Services:** club rentals, lessons, restaurant, lounge, beer, wine, liquor, pro shop. **Comments:** The course has two sets of tees for those people wanting to play a full 18 holes. The golf course is in excellent condition all year long. Company tournaments are welcome.

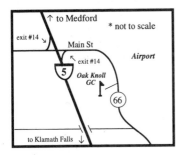

Directions: from I-5 take exit #14 (Southern Oregon State College). Head east on Hwy 66. The golf course will be located .75 miles on your right hand side. **Note:** The golf course is located across from the Ashland City Airport. Look for signs marking your way.

Course Yardage & Par:
M-3135 yards, par 36.
W-2964 yards, par 38.
<u>**Dual Tees 18 holes:**</u>
M-6262 yards, par 71.
W-5779 yards, par 74.

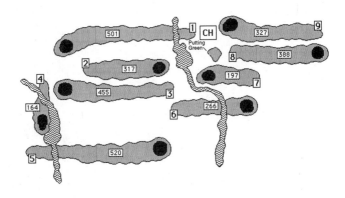

Oak Knoll Golf Course (public)
6335 Hwy 22; Independence, OR 97351; (503) 378-0344
Pro: John McComish, PGA. 18 hole course, driving range.
Rating/Slope: C 68.6/113; M 67.1/111, W 69.2/113. **Course record:** 63.
Greens fee: $20/$12 all week long; VISA, M/C.
Power cart: $20/$10. **Pull cart:** $2. **Trail fee:** $10/$5.
Reservation policy: yes, 1 day in advance. **Winter condition:** open, damp.
Terrain: flat. **Tees:** grass. **Temporary greens:** no. **Services:** club rentals,
lessons, snack bar, restaurant, lounge, beer, wine, liquor, pro shop, lockers,
driving range. **Comments:** one of the area's most popular courses.You will
always find the course in great condition. Excellent public golf course.

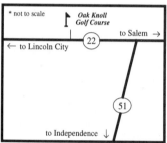

Directions: the golf course is located 7
miles west of Salem on the north side
of Hwy 22. Take exit #253 off of I-5
to Hwy 22 in Salem, Oregon. Look for
signs to the golf course.

Course Yardage & Par:
C-6208 yards, par 72.
M-5909 yards, par 72.
W-5239 yards, par 72.

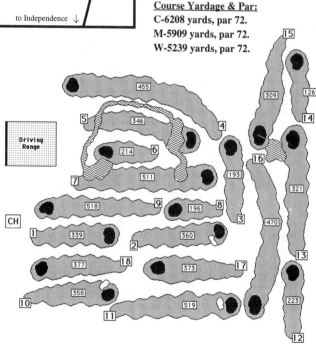

Oakway Golf Course (public)

2000 Cal Young Road; Eugene, OR 97401; (503) 484-1927
Manager: Tom DeCuman. 18 hole executive course.
Rating/Slope: M 57.0/no slope; W 57.0/no slope. **Course Record:** 55.
Greens fee: $15/$9 all week long; Jr. & Sr. rates; M/C, VISA.
Power Cart: $15/$9. **Pull Cart:** $2. **Trail fee:** personal carts are not allowed.
Reservation policy: no. **Winter condition:** open. **Terrain:** flat, some hills.
Tees: grass. **Temporary greens:** no. **Services:** club rentals, restaurant, beer,
wine, pro shop. **Comments:** One of the nicest courses in Oregon. The course
is easy to walk. Excellent course for seniors who want to play a highly competive
course but do not want the length. Fairways can play very tight at times.

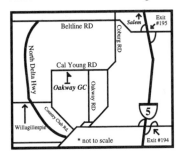

Directions: from I-5 take exit #195. Head
west on Beltline Road. Take the Coburg
Road exit and go south. At Cal Young
Road turn right. The golf course will be
1/4 mile ahead on your left hand side.

Course Yardage & Par:
M-3609 yards, par 61.
W-3117 yards, par 61.

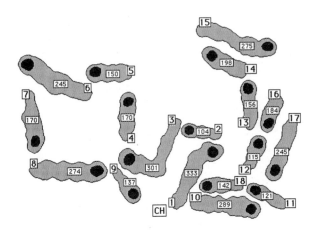

Ocean Dunes Golf Links (public)

3345 Munsel Lake Road; Florence, OR 97439; (503) 997-3232; 1-800-468-4833
Manager: Mark Shepherd. 18 hole course, driving range.
Rating/Slope: C 68.5/124; M 67.4/122; W 69.5/124. **Course record:** 68.
Greens fee: $28/$15; Sr. rates, winter rates November to March; M/C, VISA.
Power cart: $24/N/A. **Pull cart:** $3/$2. **Trail fee:** $8 for personal carts.
Reservation policy: yes, please call ahead for weekends. **Winter condition:** dry.
Terrain: flat, rolling some hills. **Tees:** grass. **Temporary greens:** no.
Services: club rentals, lessons, snack bar, beer, wine, pro shop, driving range.
Comments: This course is built on sand dunes which keeps it dry during the
winter and it plays like a real links course. Great course to play while on the coast.

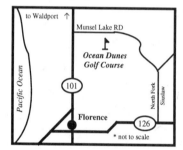

Directions: from Hwy 101 turn
eastbound on Munsel Lake Road and
proceed to the golf course. From Hwy
126 (Florence Hwy) go north on North
Fork Siuslaw. When you reach Munsel
Lake Road turn left to the golf course.
The golf course will be located on your
left hand side. Look for signs marking
your turn to the golf course.

Course Yardage & Par:
C-5670 yards, par 70.
M-5430 yards, par 70/71.
W-4868 yards, par 72.

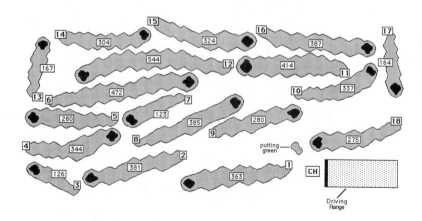

Olalla Valley Golf Course & Restaurant (public)
1022 Olalla Road; Toledo, OR 97391; (503) 336-2121
Manager: N/A. **9 hole course, dual tees for 18 holes.**
Rating/Slope: M 69.2/127; W 72.7/124. **Course record:** 63.
Greens fee: $16/$8; M/C, VISA. **Power cart:** $16/$8. **Pull cart:** $2.
Trail fee: $4/$2. **Reservation policy:** yes, required for weekend tee times.
Winter condition: open, course drains well. **Terrain:** very hilly. **Tees:** grass.
Temporary greens: no. **Services:** club rentals, restaurant, beer, wine, pro shop.
Comments: Excellent winter golf course. Nine hole golf course that has two sets of tees for 18 hole play. Water will come into play on nearly every hole. The golf course can be very demanding at times. Try playing this course while on the coast.

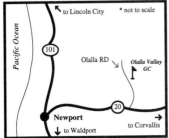

Directions: on Hwy 101 the golf course is located 6 miles east of Newport. From Hwy 20 (from Corvallis) go west 45 minutes to the golf course. Exit on to Olalla Rd. from Hwy 20. There are signs from each direction you can follow to the golf course.

Course Yardage & Par:
M-2884 yards, par 36.
W-2587 yards, par 37.
Dual Tees 18 holes:
M-5951 yards, par 72.
W-5507 yards, par 74.

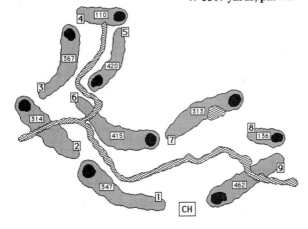

Oregon City Golf Club (public)

20124 Beaver Creek Road; Oregon City, OR 97045; (503) 656-2846
Pro: Bill Hagedorn. 18 hole course, putting green.
Rating/Slope: M 67.3/107; M65.6/103; W 65.6/103. **Course record:** 61.
Greens fee: W/D $18/$9; W/E $24/$12; Sr. rates (weekdays); M/C, VISA.
Power cart: $25/$15. **Pull cart:** $3. **Trail fee:** $5.
Reservation policy: yes, a must, 2 weeks in advance. **Winter condition:** dry.
Terrain: gentle, rolling hills. **Tees:** grass. **Temporary greens:** no.
Services: club rentals, lessons, snack bar, beer, pro shop. **Comments:** This is
one of the oldest golf courses in the state of Oregon. Excellent drainage and
good maintenance provide very dry course conditions even in winter.

Directions: from I-205 N&S take exit
10 (Park Place). Head south on Hwy
213. At the 3rd light go left (eastbound)
on Beaver Creek Road. The golf course
is located 1.5 miles ahead on your left.

Course Yardage & Par:
C-5950 yards, par 71.
M-5856 yards, par 71.
W-5709 yards, par 79.

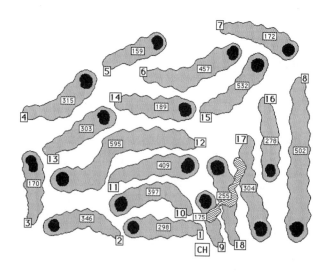

The Oregon Golf Club (private)

25700-A SW Pete's Mountain Road; West Linn, OR 97068; (503) 650-7805
Pro: Craig Griswold, PGA. **18 hole course, driving range. Course record:** 63.
Rating/Slope: J 74.4/135; C 72.1/132; M 69.8/123; W 71.1/125.
Greens fee: private club, members & guests only; limited reciprocation.
Power cart: private club. **Pull cart:** yes. **Trail fee:** not allowed.
Reservation policy: private club. **Winter condition:** open, dry.
Terrain: generously sloping terrain. **Services:** full service private facility.
Driving range. **Comments:** the course was co-designed by Peter Jacobsen. The
layout is of championship caliber with sand on nearly every hole. Host of the
annual Fred Meyer Challenge.

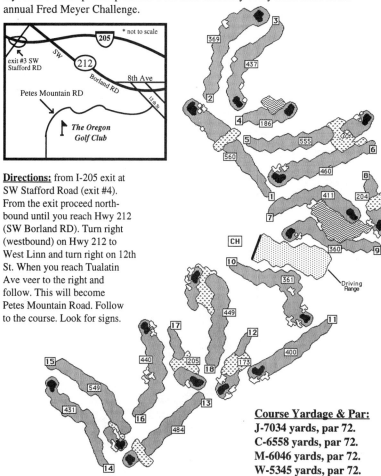

Directions: from I-205 exit at
SW Stafford Road (exit #4).
From the exit proceed north-
bound until you reach Hwy 212
(SW Borland RD). Turn right
(westbound) on Hwy 212 to
West Linn and turn right on 12th
St. When you reach Tualatin
Ave veer to the right and
follow. This will become
Petes Mountain Road. Follow
to the course. Look for signs.

Course Yardage & Par:
J-7034 yards, par 72.
C-6558 yards, par 72.
M-6046 yards, par 72.
W-5345 yards, par 72.

Orenco Woods Golf Club (public)

22200 NW Birch; PO Box 25; Hillsboro, OR 97123; (503) 648-1836
Pro: Rich Haaland, PGA. 9 hole course, dual tees for 18 holes..
Rating/Slope: M 65.9/109; W 67.3/109. **Course record:** 63.
Greens fee: $17/$9 all week long; Jr. & Sr. rates; M/C, VISA.
Power cart: $20/$10. **Pull cart:** $2. **Trail fee:** $10/$5.
Reservation policy: yes, a must for weekends. **Winter condition:** open, damp.
Terrain: very hilly. **Tees:** grass. **Temporary greens:** no. **Services:** club rentals,
lessons, snack bar, beer, pro shop, driving range. **Comments:** The golf course is
very hilly and presents a good challenge. The greens are small and put a premium
on shot making. A creek comes into play on nearly every hole.

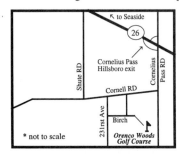

Directions: take Hwy 26 out of Portland
going west. Take Cornelius Pass/Hillsboro
exit. Proceed south on Cornelius Pass Road
to NW Cornell Road and turn right. Proceed
to NW 231st Ave. and turn left to NW
Birch. Proceed and turn left to the golf
course.

Course Yardage & Par; Dual tees 18 holes:
M-2626 yards, par 35. M-5376 yards, par 71.
W-2454 yards, par 36. W-5080 yards, par 72.

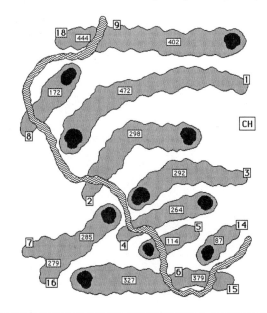

Orion Greens Golf Course (public)
61525 Fargo Lane; Bend, OR 97702; (503) 388-3999
Manager: Bud Lamarche. 9 hole executive course.
Rating/Slope: M 58.3/98; W 62.0/95. **Course record:** 26.
Greens fee: $18/$11 all week long; M/C, VISA.
Power cart: $19/$10. **Pull cart:** $2/$1. **Trail fee:** $10/$5.
Reservation policy: call for reservations. **Winter condition:** open, weather permitting. **Terrain:** flat. **Tees:** grass. **Temporary greens:** no.
Services: club rentals, lessons, snack bar, restaurant, lounge, beer, wine, liquor, putting green. **Comments:** This facility is well kept. The golf course is in excellent condition most of the year. Good walking golf course.

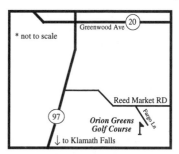

Directions: take Hwy 97. Go east on Reed Market Road. Proceed 1.5 miles to Fargo Lane. Turn right on Fargo Lane and follow this to the golf course which will be on your right hand side. Look for signs to the golf course the way is well marked.

Course Yardage & Par:
White tees: 2075 yards, par 31.
Gold tees: 1939 yards, par 31.
Red tees: 1738 yards, par 31.

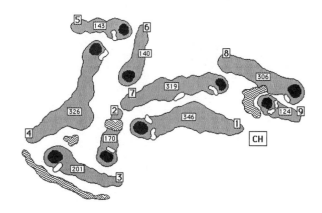

Oswego Lake Country Club (private)
20 Iron Mountain Blvd: PO Box 508; Lake Oswego, OR 97034; (503) 635-3659
Pro: Brent Murray, PGA. 18 hole course, driving range.
Rating/Slope: C 71.6/129; M 70.4/126; W 73.4/124. **Course record: 65.**
Greens fee: private club members & guests only; reciprocates; no credit cards.
Power cart: private club. **Pull cart:** private club. **Trail fee:** not allowed.
Reservation policy: yes, 2 days in advance. **Winter condition:** open, damp.
Terrain: very hilly. **Tees:** grass. **Temporary greens:** yes in winter.
Services: lessons, snack bar, restaurant, lounge, beer, wine, liquor, pro shop,
lockers, showers, driving range. **Comments:** The golf course is noted for the
many picturesque golf holes it has. Course can play very, very tough at times.

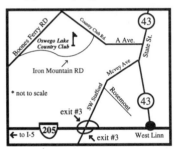

Directions: from I-5 take Hwy 217 exit into Lake Oswego. Take left onto Boones Ferry then a right onto Country Club. Take right onto Iron Mountain Boulevard the course will be on your right hand side. From I-205 exit to go north at either Pacific Hwy 43 Willamette Drive or at SW Stafford and proceed north to State and turn left onto "A" Ave to Country Club Road to the golf course.

Course Yardage & Par:
C-6432 yards, par 71.
M-6200 yards, par 71.
W-5726 yards, par 73.

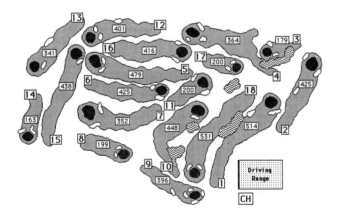

Pendleton Country Club (private)
off of Hwy 395; Route 2, Box 94; Pendleton, OR 97801; (503) 278-1739
Pro: Doug Newman, PGA. 18 hole course, driving range.
Rating/Slope: C 69.5/115; M 68.2/111; W 70.3/117. **Course record:** 64.
Greens fee: private club members & guests only; reciprocates; M/C, VISA.
Power cart: private club. **Pull cart:** private club. **Trail fee:** private club.
Reservation policy: private club members & guests only.
Winter condition: open. **Terrain:** flat. **Tees:** grass. **Temporary greens:** no.
Services: club rentals, lessons, snack bar, restaurant, lounge, beer, wine,
liquor, pro shop, showers, driving range. **Comments:** The course is well
conditioned during the golf season. Lush fairways with medium to fast greens.

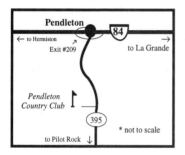

Directions: the golf course is located 8
miles south of Pendleton. From I-84
E&W take exit #209 to Hwy 395. Follow
Hwy 395 for 7.7 miles to the golf course
on your right hand side.

Course Yardage & Par:
C-6302 yards, par 72.
M-6060 yards, par 72.
W-5483 yards, par 74.

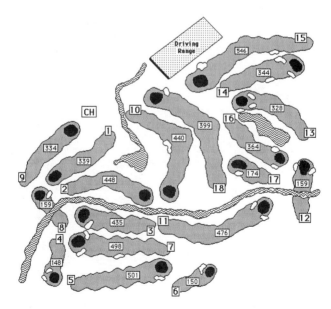

Persimmon Country Club (semi-private)
8015 SE Hogan Road; Gresham, OR 97080; (503) 667-7500
Pro: Larry Skreen, PGA. 18 hole course. Course record: 68.
Rating/Slope: C 71.2/125; M 69.5/122; W 70.3/122.
Greens fee: W/D $45; W/E $55. **Power cart:** $22/$11. **Pull cart:** $4/$2.
Trail fee: not allowed. **Reservation policy:** members 7 days in advance; non
members 24 hour advance. **Winter condition:** open. **Terrain:** gently sloping.
Tees: grass. **Services:** club rentals, lessons, swing analysis, outdoor practice cages,
pro shop, club repair, driving range, grill room with beer & wine, lockers.
Comments: golf course designed by Bunny Mason with incredible views of the
Cascade Mountains. Great new golf course that will challenge you at every turn.

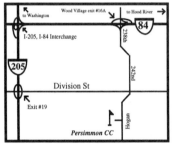

Directions: from I-84 take the Wood
Village exit and go south on 238th. 238th
will become 242nd, then becomes Hogan
Road. Proceed to the golf course which
will be located on your right. The golf
course is approximately 4.5 miles from
your I-84 exit. Look for signs marking your
way to the golf course.

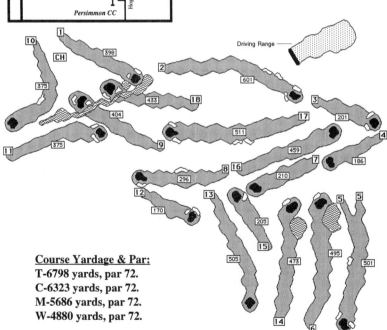

Course Yardage & Par:
T-6798 yards, par 72.
C-6323 yards, par 72.
M-5686 yards, par 72.
W-4880 yards, par 72.

Pineway Golf Course (public)

30949 Pineway Road; Lebanon, OR 97355; (503) 258-8815
Pros: Jim Glasser, Mickie Price. 9 hole course, dual tees for 18 holes.
Rating/Slope: M 68.1/108; W 73.8/ 122. **Course record:** 64.
Greens fee: W/D $17/$9*; W/E $18/$10*; Jr. & Sr. rates (weekdays); M/C, VISA.
Power cart: $18/$10*. **Pull cart:** $2*. **Trail fee:** $9/$5*. (*subject to change).
Reservation policy: yes, 1 week in advance. **Winter condition:** open, dry.
Terrain: relatively hilly. **Tees:** grass. **Services:** club rentals, lessons, restaurant,
lounge, beer, wine, pro shop, snack bar, lockers, driving range, practice green.
Comments: course is in great shape all year round. Dual tees will give you a
different look if you are playing a full 18 holes of golf. New 9 in planning stages.

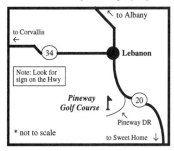

Directions: the golf course is located
just off of Hwy 20 4.3 miles southeast
of Lebanon, Oregon. A large sign will
indicate the course as well as the restaurant.

Course Yardage & Par:
M-2967 yards, par 36.
W-2960 yards, par 37.
Dual tees 18 holes:
M-5927 yards, par 72.
W-5919 yards, par 74.

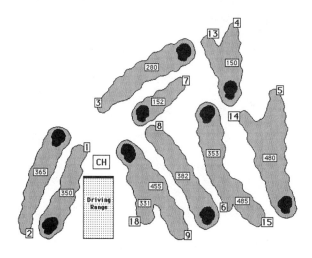

Pleasant Valley Golf Club (private)
12300 SE 162nd Avenue; Clackamas, OR 97105; (503) 658-3101
Pro: Jim Smith, PGA. 18 hole course, driving range.
Rating/Slope: C 71.9/128; M 70.7/125; W 71.9/121. **Course record**: 66.
Greens fee: private club, members & guests only; reciprocates.
Power cart: private club. **Pull cart**: private club. **Trail fee**: not allowed.
Reservation policy: private club members only. **Winter condition**: open, dry.
Terrain: flat, some hills. **Tees**: grass. **Temporary greens**: no.
Services: club rentals, lessons, snack bar, restaurant, beer, wine, liquor,
pro shop, lockers. **Comments**: private club, members and guests only.
Course is well conditioned, and offers challenging golf. Great golf course.

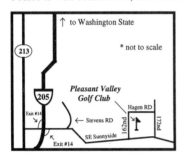

Directions: from Hwy 205 exit
eastbound on Milwaukie-Foster Road
which becomes SE Sunnyside. Follow
for 3.4 mi to 162nd and turn left for .5
mi to the golf course on your right.
Note: sign indicating your turn.

Course Yardage & Par:
C-6593 yards, par 72.
M-6164 yards, par 72.
W-5410 yards, par 73.

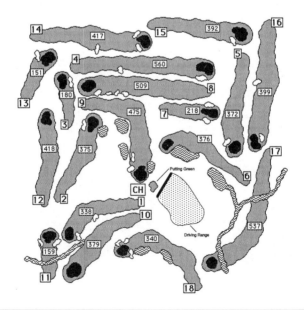

Portland Golf Club (private)

5900 SW Scholls Ferry Road; Portland, OR 97225; (503) 292-2778
Pro: Larry Lamberger Jr., PGA. 18 hole course, driving range.
Rating/Slope: C 72.4/131; M 70.8/127; W 74.0/127. **Course record:** 64.
Greens fee: private, limited reciprocation (must be cleared by head pro).
Power cart: private club members only. **Pull cart:** private club members only.
Reservation policy: private club members and guests only.
Winter condition: open, damp. **Terrain:** relatively hilly. **Tees:** grass.
Services: club rentals, lessons, snack bar, restaurant, lounge, beer, wine, liquor,
pro shop, lockers, showers, driving range. **Comments:** Beautiful, old, historical
golf course. Home to numerous past major tournaments, P.G.A., Ryder Cup,
Western Open, U.S. Senior open. The golf course is rated #3 in the state of Oregon.

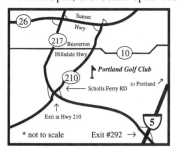

Directions: from I-5 take exit # 217.
Follow SW Scholls Ferry Road and
proceed 3 miles north to the golf course.

Course Yardage & Par:
C-6683 yards, par 72.
M-6323 yards, par 72.
W-5868 yards, par 73.

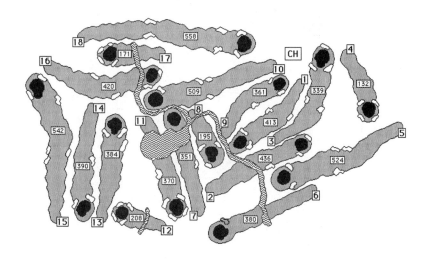

Portland Meadows Golf Course (public)
901 N Schmeer Road; Portland, OR 97217; (503) 289-3405
Pro: teaching pro during the summer. 9 hole executive course, driving range.
Rating/Slope: the golf course is not rated. **Course record: 57.**
Greens fee: Monday's $4.50; Tuesday thru Friday $6; Sat., Sun. & Holidays $7.
Power cart: none available. **Pull cart:** $2. **Trail fee:** not allowed.
Reservation policy: no. **Winter condition:** October to April, open at 10am
Monday thru Friday. Closed weekends and holidays for horse racing.
Terrain: flat. **Tees:** grass. **Temporary greens:** no. **Services:** club rentals, snack
bar, beer, driving range, lessons, limited pro shop. **Comments:** Unusual setting.
The golf course is situated in the center of the Portland Meadows horse racing track.

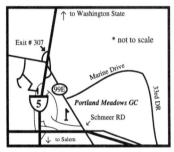

Directions: from I-5 N&S take exit # 306B
(Delta Park). Turn left at the stop sign on
North Victory Boulevard. Get in the right
hand lane. Curve to the right for 1/2 mile to
North Schmeer Road. The golf course will
be located .2 miles ahead to your left at the
race track. **Note:** Look for the Portland
Meadows race track and you will find the
golf course. Also look for signs along the
way. The course is well marked.

Course Yardage & Par:
M-1983 yards, par 31; W-1983 yards, par 35.

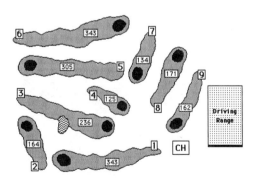

Prineville Golf & Country Club (private)

232204 E Highway 26; Prineville, OR 97754; (503) 447-7225
Pro: Jeff Bright, PGA. 9 hole course, dual tees for 18 holes.
Rating/Slope: M 64.1/112; W 65.9/107. **Course record:** 59.
Greens fee: private club, reciprocates call in advance; M/C, VISA.
Power cart: private club. **Pull cart:** private club. **Trail fee:** private club.
Reservation policy: no. **Winter condition:** dry. **Terrain:** flat, some hills.
Tees: grass. **Temporary greens:** no. **Services:** rentals, lessons, snack bar,
restaurant, lounge, beer, wine, liquor, pro shop, showers, driving range.
Comments: in excellent condition April through September. The golf course
is very beautiful, tricky but fair. Separate tees for 18 hole play. Good course.

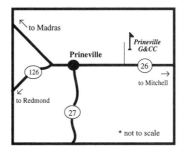

Directions: the golf course is located 3
mile east of Prineville off of Hwy 26.
Look for a sign marking your entrance
to the Country Club.

Course Yardage & Par:
M-2525 yards, par 33.
W-2268 yards, par 34.
Dual Tees 18 holes:
M-4959 yards, par 65.
W-4662 yards, par 68.

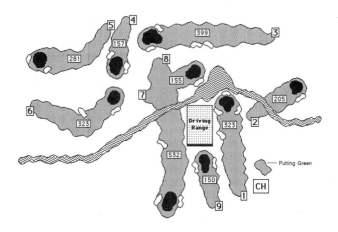

Progress Downs Municipal Golf Course (public)
8200 Scholls Ferry Road; Beaverton, OR 97005; (503) 646-5166
Pro: Jerry Minor, PGA. 18 hole course, covered & lighted driving range.
Rating/Slope: C 69.8/112; M 68.4/110; W 71.7/115. **Course record:** 62.
Greens fee: W/D $13/$7*; W/E $15/$8*; Jr. & Sr. rates. (*prices will change)
Power cart: $20/$10*; **Pull cart:** $3/$2*. **Trail Fee:** $3*.
Reservation policy: yes. **Winter condition:** open, dry. **Terrain:** flat, some
hills. **Tees:** grass. **Temporary greens:** no. **Services:** rentals, lessons, restaurant,
lounge, pro shop, driving range. **Comments:** well kept facility. Driving range is
double decked and is lighted. Great public golf center that includes a fantastic on
course pro shop that will meet all your golfing needs. Excellent public facility.
The course will undergo remodeling during 1994. The course will still be open
for play with the existing tee boxes and greens. Very popular golfing facility.

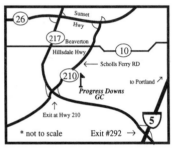

Directions: Hwy 217 exit at Progress exit.
Go left on SW Hall Boulevard. Take first
left at the light after proceeding over the
overpass onto Scholls Ferry Road. Go for
.3 miles to the golf course on your right.

<u>**Course Yardage & Par:**</u>
C-6426 yards, par 71.
M-6122 yards, par 71.
W-5626 yards, par 73.

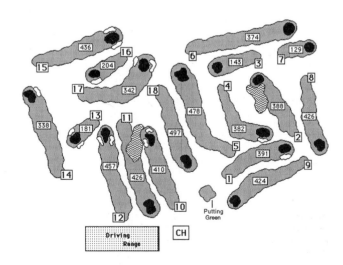

Pumpkin Ridge G.C. Ghost Creek @ Pumpkin Ridge (semi-private)

12930 NW Old Pumpkin Ridge Road; Cornelius, OR 97113-6147
Director of Golf: Jerry Mowlds, PGA. 18 hole course. (503) 647-4747, 647-9977.
Rating/Slope: T 73.8/140; C 72.1/136; M 69.4/130; W 72.1/121.
Course record: 65. **Greens fee:** M-Thur. $60; F-Sun. $75. **Power cart:** $24.
Pull cart: $3. **Reservation policy:** yes, 6 days in person, 7 days by phone.
Winter condition: open, dry, drains well. **Terrain:** gently rolling foothills.
Tees: bentgrass. **Services:** club rentals, lessons, restaurant, beer, wine, liquor, pro
shop, driving range. **Comments:** *Golf Digest's* best new public golf course for 1992.
Robert Cupp Design. Pumpkin Ridge will host the 1996 US Amateur and the 1997
US Womens Open Championships. Outstanding accommodations for tournaments.

Directions: From Hwy 26 (Sunset Hwy)
take Dersham exit. Proceed north for .3
miles, take right onto Mountaindale Road,
proceed east for 1.0 miles, take a left onto
Old Pumpkin Ridge Road. Proceed for .3
miles to the entrance on your right.

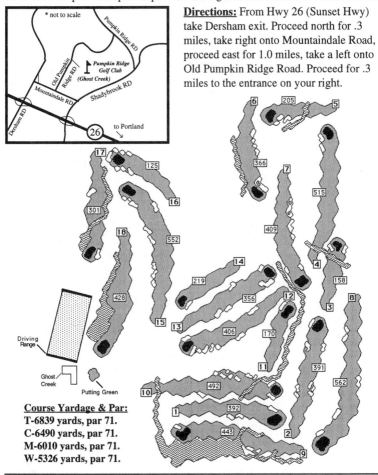

Course Yardage & Par:
T-6839 yards, par 71.
C-6490 yards, par 71.
M-6010 yards, par 71.
W-5326 yards, par 71.

Pumpkin Ridge G.C. Witch Hollow @ Pumpkin Ridge (private)

12930 NW Old Pumpkin Ridge Road; Cornelius, OR 97113-6147
Director of Golf: Jerry Mowlds, PGA. 18 hole course. (503) 647-4747, 647-2500.
Rating/Slope: T 75.1/144; C 72.3/137; M 70.2/131; W 70.4/121.
Course record: 64. **Greens fee:** private club, members only. **Power cart:** private.
Pull cart: yes. **Trail fee:** not allowed. **Reservation policy:** private club.
Winter condition: open, dry. **Terrain:** flat, some hills. **Tees:** bentgrass.
Services: club rentals, lessons, restaurant, beer, wine, liquor, pro shop, driving range.
Comments: *"Golf Digest's* 2nd best new private course for 1992". Robert Cupp design. The course sports bentgrass tees, fairways and greens. Pumpkin Ridge will host the 1996 US Amateur and the 1997 US Womens Open Championships.

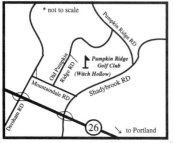

Directions: From Hwy 26 (Sunset Hwy) take Dersham exit. Proceed north for .3 miles, take right onto Mountaindale Road, proceed east for 1.0 miles, take a left onto Old Pumpkin Ridge Road. Proceed for .3 miles to the entrance on your right.

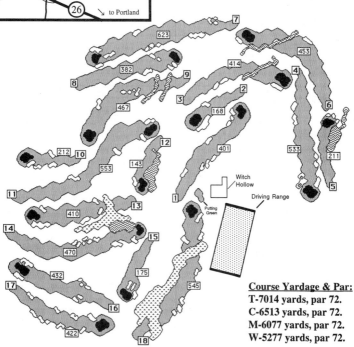

Course Yardage & Par:
T-7014 yards, par 72.
C-6513 yards, par 72.
M-6077 yards, par 72.
W-5277 yards, par 72.

Quail Point Golf Course (semi-private)
1200 Mira Mar; Medford, OR 97504; (503) 857-7000
Pro: Tom Kohler. 9 hole course, driving range.
Rating/Slope: C 69.8/126; M 68.8/123; W N/A. **Course record:** 30.
Greens fee: $20/12. **Power cart:** $18/$10. **Pull cart:** $2 (all day). **Trail fee:** N/A.
Reservation policy: may call 10 days in advance. **Winter condition:** open,
weather permitting. **Terrain:** relatively hilly. **Tees:** grass. **Temporary greens:** no.
Services: club rentals, lessons, snack bar, pro shop, driving range.
Comments: This is a very challenging new nine hole course which opened in Aug.
1993. The course offers resort conditions year round. Water comes into play on
6 holes. The hilly terrain makes this course play longer than yardage indicates.

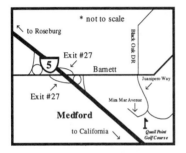

Directions: From I-5 N&S take exit #27
in Medford to Barnett Road. Travel east
to Black Oak. Turn right on Black Oak to
Juanipero. Turn right on Mira Mar Avenue.
There will be signs to the golf course that
you can follow at the top of the hill.

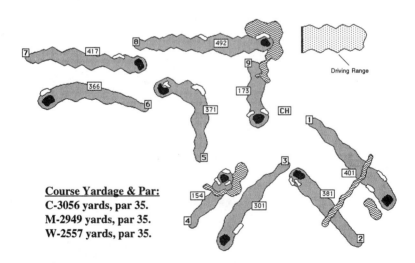

Course Yardage & Par:
C-3056 yards, par 35.
M-2949 yards, par 35.
W-2557 yards, par 35.

Quail Run Golf Course (public)

16725 Northridge Drive; PO Box 1410; La Pine, OR 97739; (503) 536-1303
Pro: Jon Noack, PGA. Owners: Jerry & Cathy Larsen. 9 hole course.
Rating/Slope: C 72.2/126; M 70.9/123; M 69.6/119 W 69.6/116.
Course Record: 33. Greens fee: $25/$15. Power cart: $18/$10. **Pull cart:** $3/$2.
Trail fee: $5. Reservation policy: yes, please call ahead for a starting time.
Winter condition: open, weather permitting. **Terrain:** flat, some undulations.
Tees: grass. **Temporary greens:** no. **Services:** club rentals, lessons, coffee shop,
beer, wine, pro shop, driving range, putting & chipping greens. **Comments:** USGA
spec built greens. Very scenic golf course with views of Mt. Bachelor and the
surrounding countryside. Excellent golf course to play in Central Oregon.

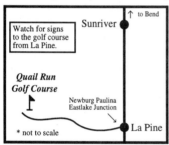

Directions: the golf course is located 8
miles south of Sunriver Oregon. Turn
right on Newburg Paulina Eastlake
Junction. Cross the RR tracks and follow
signs to the golf course.

Course Yardage & Par:
C-3450 yards, par 36.
M-3166 yards, par 36.
M-3014 yards, par 36.
W-2707 yards, par 36.

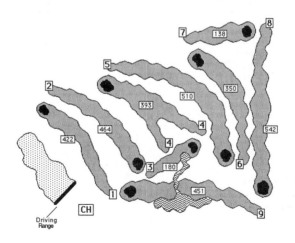

Quail Valley Golf Course (public)

12565 NW Aerts Road; Banks, OR 97106; (503) 324-4444
Pro: Doug Hixson. 18 hole course, driving range.
Rating/Slope: C 71.6/122; M 68.9/114; W 71.5/117. **Course record:** N/A.
Greens fee: Mon.-Thur. $25/$13; Fri.-Sun. & Hol. $27/$14. **Power cart:** $22/$11.
Pull cart: $3/$1.50. **Trail fee:** N/A. **Reservation policy:** please call in advance
for tee times. **Winter condition:** open, weather permitting. **Terrain:** beautifully
mounded. **Tees:** grass. **Temporary greens:** no. **Services:** fully stocked pro shop,
club rentals, lessons, lounge, snack bar, driving range. **Comments:** A beautiful
newer course that is worth a special trip. Four lakes, 12 surface acres of water,
600 small trees, and 44 bunkers will challenge your golfing skill at every turn.

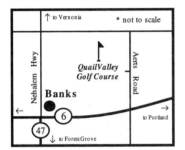

Directions: From Portland, Oregon take
highway 26 westbound to highway 6. Exit
onto highway 6 and proceed to Banks,
Oregon. Proceed to NW Aerts Road. Turn
on NW Aerts Road and proceed to the golf
course. Look for signs marking your way
to the golf course.

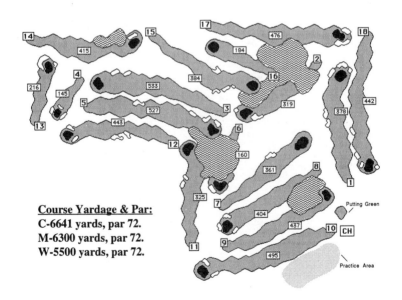

Course Yardage & Par:
C-6641 yards, par 72.
M-6300 yards, par 72.
W-5500 yards, par 72.

Ranch Hills Golf Club (public)

26710 S Ranch Hills Road; Mulino, OR 97042; (503) 632-6848
Owners: Dewey Wyatt. 9 hole course, putting green.
Rating/Slope: M 63.3/96; W 67.2/101. **Course record:** 29/59.
Greens fee: W/D $16/$8; W/E $18/$9; Sr. rates; no credit cards.
Power cart $20/10. **Pull cart:** $1.50. **Trail fee:** $3.
Reservation policy: yes. **Winter condition:** open. **Terrain:** flat.
Tees: grass. **Temporay greens:** no. **Services:** rentals, snack bar, beer, wine,
pro shop. **Comments:** closed Thursdays after 12 noon and Saturdays until noon.
Mill Creek wanders throughout this nine hole golf course putting an emphasis on
accuracy off the tee. Golf course can play very tight at times.

Directions: from Hwy 213 S turn left on
Passmore Road. Proceed straight ahead
for 1.3 miles to the golf course. From
Hwy 213 N turn right on Passmore Road.
Make sure you look for a sign marking
your way to the golf course.

Course Yardage & Par:
C-3135 yards, par 36.
M-2838 yards, par 36.
W-2636 yards, par 37.

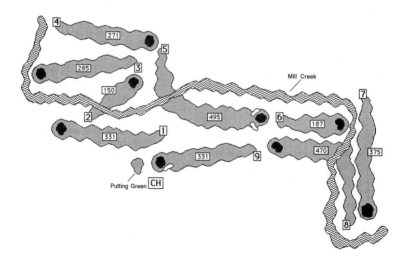

Reames Golf & Country Club (private)

4201 Hwy 97 South; Klamath Falls, OR 97603; (503) 884-7446
Pro: Mike Oberlander, PGA. 18 hole course.
Rating/Slope: C 71.2/124; M 70.3/123; W 73.3/127. **Course Record**: 65.
Greens fee: private club, members & guests only; reciprocates; no credit cards.
Power Cart: private club. **Pull Cart**: private club. **Trail fee**: private club.
Reservation policy: yes, 1 week in advance. **Winter condition**: good.
Terrain: flat, some hills. **Tees**: grass. **Temporary greens**: no.
Services: club rentals, lessons, restaurant, lounge, beer, wine, pro shop,
lockers, showers, driving range. **Comments:** This is an outstanding golf
facility. Tough greens make this course a good test of your golf game.

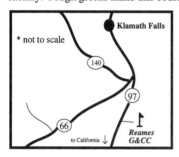

Directions: course is located off of Hwy
97 south of Klamath Falls. You can see
the golf course from the Hwy. You will
turn eastbound to get to the clubhouse
from Hwy 97.

Course Yardage & Par:
C-6564 yards, par 72.
M-6371 yards, par 72.
W-5855 yards, par 74.

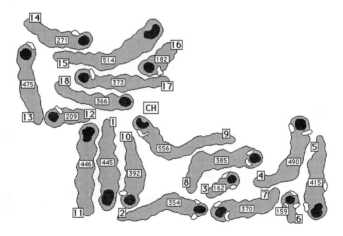

Red Mountain Golf Course (public)

324 North Schoolhouse Creek Road; Grants Pass, OR 97526; (503) 479-2297
Owner: Dave Snook. 9 hole executive course, dual tees for 18 holes.
Rating/Slope: the golf course is not rated. **Course record:** 58.
Greens fee: $10/$6; Monday-Friday play all day for $14. (*subject to change).
Power cart: not available. **Pull cart:** $1*. **Trail fee:** not allowed.
Reservation policy: yes, please call ahead for reservations. **Terrain:** flat, some
hills. **Tees:** grass. **Temporary greens:** no. **Services:** club rentals, beer, snack bar,
limited pro shop. **Comments:** formerly Shoestring Golf Course this executive
tract sports tree lined fairways and challenging golf. This family run course is a
bright spot on the southern Oregon golf scene. Worth a trip if in the area.

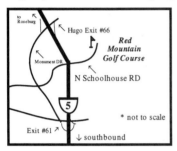

Directions: From I-5 N&S take the Merlin
or Hugo exit. Proceed to Monument Drive.
Follow to North Schoolhouse Road. Turn
eastbound and follow this to the golf course.

Course Yardage & par:
M-1118 yards, par 28.
W-1118 yards, par 28.
Dual Tees 18 holes:
M-2245 yards, par 57.
W-2245 yards, par 57.

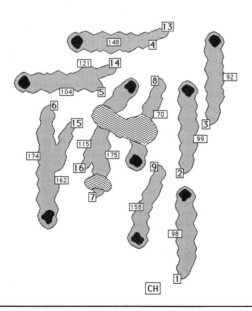

Resort at the Mountain, The (public)
68010 E Fairway Avenue; Welches, OR 97067; 800-669-4653
Pro: Rick Seven, PGA. 27 hole course. Course Record: N/A.
Greens fee: M-Th $29/$20; Fri-Sun $34/$20; M/C, VISA, AMEX, DIS.
Power Cart: $25/$15. **Pull Cart:** $4/$2. **Trail fee:** not allowed.
Reservation policy: yes, two weeks in advance, maximum.
Winter condition: open. **Terrain:** flat, some hills. **Tees:** grass.
Temporary greens: no. **Services:** club rentals, lessons, snack bar, restaurant,
lounge, beer, wine, liquor, pro shop, lockers, showers, driving range, complete
resort facility. **Comments:** These 27 holes wander through an alpine setting.
Course is in excellent condition all year round. A must play if you have time.

Directions: from Hwy 84 proceed
east to the Woodvillage exit to Hwy 26.
Proceed east to Welches. South on
Welches Rd to the golf course.

Rating/Slope:
Thistle/Foxglove: M 70/119; W 74/123.
Foxglove/Pine Cone: M 68/116; W 70/116.
Pine Cone/Thistle: M 68/114; W 70/115.

Course Yardage & Par:
Thistle Nine:
M-3351 yards, par 36. W-2954yards, par 37.
Fox Glove Nine:
M-3092/3062 yards, par 36. W-2739 yards, par 37.
Pine Cone Nine:
M-2681/2626 yards, par 34. W-2292/2071 yards, par 34.

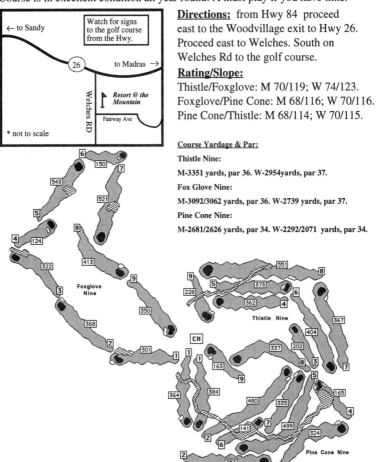

Rivergreens Golf (private)

19825 River Road; Gladstone, OR 97027. (503) 656-1033
Pro: none. 9 hole executive course.
Rating/Slope: the golf course is not rated. **Course record:** 25.
Greens fee: private, members & guests only.
Power cart: none. **Pull cart:** none. **Trail fee:** not allowed.
Reservation policy: private club. **Winter condition:** open. **Terrain:** flat.
Tees: grass. **Temporary greens:** yes. **Services:** pro shop, driving range.
Comments: Short executive course that will challenge your short game.
Excellent walking golf course. The golf course is located next to the Willamette
River in a beautiful part of Oregon. Private golf course that has no public play.

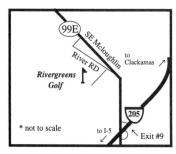

Directions: from I-205 take exit #9 onto
Hwy 99E to Gladstone. Go for .7 mi
across bridge to light where you veer left
onto River Road. Follow River Road to
the entrance immediately on your left
hand side. Look for signs marking your
way to the golf course.

Course Yardage & Par:
M-1480 yards, par 28.
W-1480 yard, par 28.

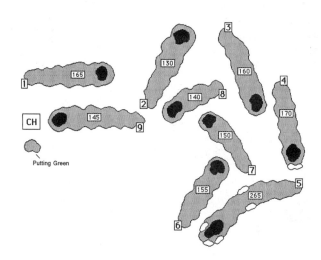

Riveridge Golf Course (public)
3800 N Delta; Eugene, OR 97401; (503) 345-9160
Pro: Ric Jeffries, PGA. Pro: Al Mundle. 18 hole course, covered range.
Rating/Slope: C 68.6/116; M 67.2/112; W 67.7/112. **Course record:** 66.
Greens fee: $21/$14*; Sr. rates; M/C, VISA. **Power cart:** $17/$10*.
Pull cart: $2*. **Trail fee:** N/A. **Reservation policy:** yes, 7 days in advance.
Winter condition: open. **Terrain:** flat, some hills. **Tees:** grass. (*will change).
Temporary greens: no. **Services:** club rentals, lessons, snack bar, beer, pro shop,
driving range. **Comments:** the golf course has a covered and lighted driving range.
The golf course is kept in excellent condition and is worth a stop if in the area.
Complete practice facility with putting, chipping greens and practice bunkers.

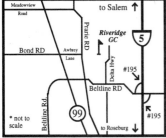

Directions: from I-5 N&S take (exit 195)
go west on Beltline to Delta Highway.
Go north on Delta Highway for 1.5 miles
to the golf course which will be located on
your left hand side of the road. Look for
signs marking your way to the golf course.

Course Yardage & Par:
C-6262 yards, par 72.
M-6007 yards, par 72.
M-5560 yards, par 72.
W-5197 yards, par 72.

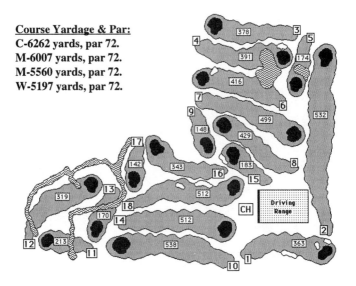

River's Edge Golf Course (public)

200 NW Mount Washington Drive; Bend, OR 97701; (503) 389-2828
Pro: Dan Heater, PGA. 18 hole course, driving range. Course record: 69.
Rating/Slope: C 72.2/139; M 71.3/137; M 69.8/133; W 71.8/135.
Greens fee: $32/$18; winter, Jr. rates; M/C, VISA. **Power cart:** $25/$15.
Pull cart: $4/$2. **Trail fee:** not allowed. **Reservation policy:** public, 1 week;
hotel guests, 30 days. **Winter condition:** course possibly closed from Jan. to Feb.
depending on conditions. **Terrain:** flat, some hills. **Tees:** grass. **Temporary
greens:** no. **Services:** club rentals, lessons, snack bar, beer, wine, pro shop,
driving range. **Comments:** course is challenging and narrow. Very scenic in its
layout. Picturesque waterfalls and serene river backdrops. Worth a trip if in Bend.

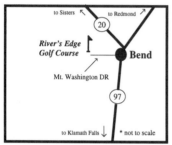

Directions: from Hwy 97, turn into the
road at the south end of the Riverhouse
Motor Inn. Golf course will be ahead.
Course located at the north end of Bend.

Course Yardage & Par:
C-6647 yards, par 72.
M-6428 yards, par 72.
M-6128 yards, par 72.
W-5380 yards, par 73.

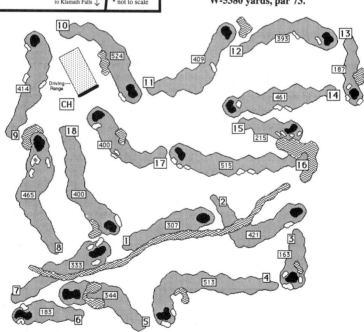

Riverside Golf & Country Club (private)
8105 NE 33rd Drive; Portland, OR 97211; (503) 282-7265
Pro: Pat Sutton, PGA. 18 hole course. Course record: 65.
Rating/Slope: C 72.2/129; M 71.4/128; M 70.4/125 W 74.0/126.
Greens fee: private club, members & guests only; M/C, VISA.
Power cart: private club. **Pull cart:** private club. **Trail fee:** not allowed.
Reservation policy: private club, members only. **Winter condition:** open.
Terrain: flat. **Tees:** grass. **Temporary greens:** no. **Services:** club rentals, lessons,
restaurant, lounge, beer, wine, liquor, pro shop, lockers, showers, driving range.
Comments: Mature trees abound at this picturesque course. One of Portland's
best private clubs. Course plays very tough in places. Excellent golf course.

Directions: from I-5 take the Columbia
St. exit and go eastbound to NE 33rd. Turn
left to the golf course. From I-205 take the
Columbia St. exit and go westbound for 2
miles to NE 33rd. Turn right to the course.

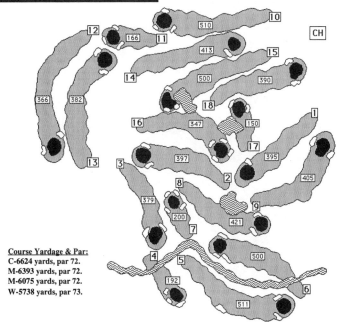

Course Yardage & Par:
C-6624 yards, par 72.
M-6393 yards, par 72.
M-6075 yards, par 72.
W-5738 yards, par 73.

Riverwood Golf Course (public)

21050 SE Riverwood Road; Dundee, OR 97115; (503) 864-2667
Pro: Gregory C. Brown, PGA. 9 hole course, dual tees for 18 holes.
Rating/Slope: M 67.4/117; W 69.3/118. **Course record:** 65.
Greens fee: $18/$9.50; Jr. & Sr. rates, during weekdays only; no credit cards.
Power cart: $16/$8. **Pull cart:** $1.50. **Trail fee:** $8/$4.
Reservation policy: yes. **Winter condition:** open, damp. **Terrain:** flat.
Tees: grass. **Temporary greens:** N/A. **Services:** club rentals, lessons,
snack bar, beer, wine, pro shop, driving range. **Comments:** Course is flat
and very easy to walk. The course was built in 1932 and displays many
mature trees. Recent improvements make for a challenging nine hole round.

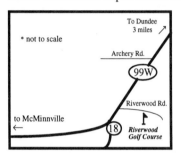

Directions: the golf course is located
1 mile off of Hwy 99W. After traveling
3 miles on Hwy 99W look for Riverwood
Road. Turn right to the golf course. Look
for a sign on the east side of the Hwy.
The golf course located south of Newburg.

Course Yardage & Par:
M-2861 yards, par 35.
W-2637 yards, par 36.
Dual tees 18 holes:
M-5807 yards, par 70.
W-5434 yards, par 72.

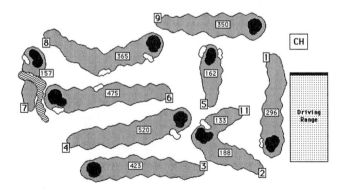

Rock Creek Country Club (private)

5100 NW Neakahnie; Portland, OR 97213; (503) 645-1101
Pro: Scott Nash, PGA. 18 hole course, driving range.
Rating/Slope: C 71.9/123; M 71.0/122; W 72.5/125. **Course record:** 63.
Greens fee: private, members only; reciprocates; M/C, VISA.
Power cart: private club. **Pull cart:** private club. **Trail fee:** no charge.
Reservation policy: private club, members and guests only.
Winter condition: open, dry. **Terrain:** flat. **Tees:** grass. **Temporary greens:** no.
Services: club rentals, lessons, restaurant, lounge, beer, wine, liquor, pro shop,
lockers, showers, driving range. **Comments:** Beautiful private club in Portland.
The course sports several ponds and greenside bunkers to catch any errant shots.

Directions: from I-5 exit on Hwy 26
(Sunset Hwy W). Go 10 miles to 185th.
Turn north on 185th and proceed
approximately 1.5 miles to the West
Union Road Intersection. Turn left.
Travel west for .5 miles to Neakahnie
and the golf course.

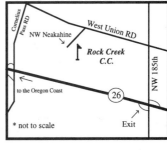

Course Yardage & Par:
C-6634 yards, par 72.
M-6371 yards, par 72.
W-5629 yards, par 74.

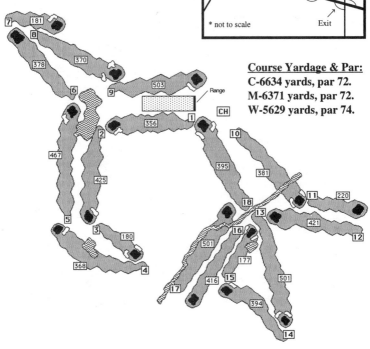

Rogue Valley Country Club (private)

2660 Hillcrest Road; Medford, OR 97504; (503) 772-4050
Pro: Jim Wise, PGA. 27 hole course, driving range. Course record: 63.
Greens fee: private club; reciprocates ; M/C,VISA. **Power cart:** private.
Pull cart: $3/$2. **Reservation policy:** 2 days in advance. **Winter condition:** open.
Terrain: flat, some hills. **Tees:** grass. **Services:** club rentals, lessons, snack bar,
restaurant, lounge, beer, wine, liquor, pro shop, lockers, showers, driving range.
Comments: Host of the Southern Oregon Golf Championship. Great golf course.

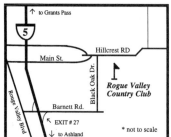

Directions: from I-5 take the Barnett exit.
Travel east on Barnett to Black Oak RD,
turn left. Proceed straight to Hillcrest RD.
Turn right on Hillcrest Road to the course.

Course Yardage & Par:
Original Course:
C-6724 yards, par 72.
M-6394 yards, par 72.
W-5979 yards, par 75.

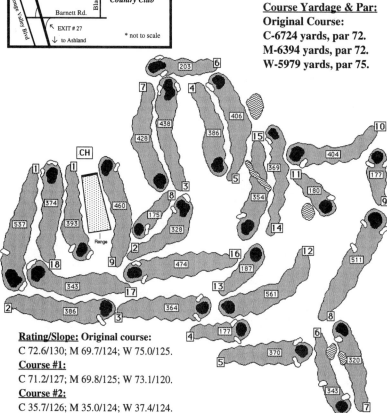

Rating/Slope: Original course:
C 72.6/130; M 69.7/124; W 75.0/125.
Course #1:
C 71.2/127; M 69.8/125; W 73.1/120.
Course #2:
C 35.7/126; M 35.0/124; W 37.4/124.

Rose City Golf Course (public)

2200 NE 71st Ave; Portland, OR 97213; (503) 253-4744, 292-8570 for T-times
Pro: Hank Childs, PGA. 18 hole course. Course record: 64.
Rating/Slope: C 70.6/118; M 69.3/114; W 75.1/128; W 71.6/117.
Greens fee: W/D $15/$8; W/E $17/$9; Jr./Sr. rates; non residents add $2.
Power cart: $22/$11. Pull cart: $3/$2. Trail fee: $4/$2.
Reservation policy: yes, call five days in advance or visit a week in advance.
Winter condition: open, dry. Terrain: flat, some hills. Tees: grass.
Temporary greens: no. Services: club rentals, lessons, snack bar, restaurant,
beer, wine, pro shop. **Comments:** Beautiful old clubhouse surrounded by mature
trees. The golf course is in kept in excellent condition throughout the year.

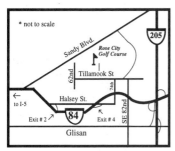

Directions: from I-84 eastbound take exit
#4 (68th Avenue) and travel straight on
NE Hasley St for .3 miles to NE 74th.
Turn left on 74th and proceed .3 miles to
Tillamook. Turn left, the golf course will
be on your right hand side. Look for signs.

Course Yardage & Par:
C-6455 yards, par 72.
M-6166 yards, par 72.
W-5619 yards, par 74.

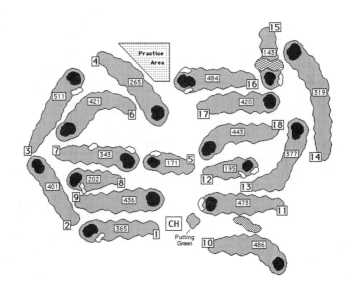

Roseburg Country Club (private)

5051 NW Garden Valley Road; Roseburg, OR 97470. (503) 672-4041.
Pro: Pat Huffer, PGA. 18 hole course, driving range.
Rating/Slope: C 70.5/125; M 68.9/119; W 70.8/116. **Course record: 62.**
Greens fee: private, members only; reciprocates.
Power cart: private club. **Pull cart:** private club. **Trail fee:** private club.
Reservation policy: yes, up to 2 weeks in advance. **Winter condition:** open, damp.
Terrain: some hills, with flat areas. **Tees:** grass. **Temporary greens:** no.
Services: club rentals, lessons, snack bar, restaurant, lounge, beer, wine, liquor,
pro shop, lockers, showers, driving range, pool. **Comments:** Relatively short
course with well bunkered, undulating greens. No one ever "tears this course up".

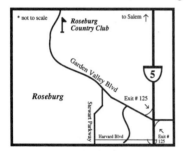

Directions: from I-5 take exit #125 at
Roseburg (Garden Valley). Travel west
for 4.5 miles on NW Garden Valley Road
to the golf course which will be on your
right hand side.

<u>**Course Yardage & Par:**</u>
C-6316 yards, par 71.
M-5965 yards, par 71.
W-5529 yards, par 72.

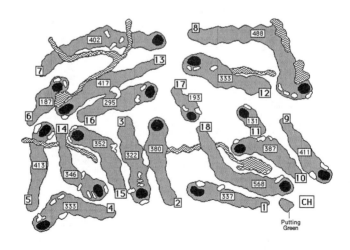

Roseburg VA Hospital Golf Course (private)

Stewart Park, E Stewart Parkway; Roseburg, OR 97470; no phone.
Pro: none. 9 hole course.
Rating/Slope: the golf course is not rated. **Course record:** 33.
Greens fee: private club; for patient and staff use only.
Power cart: none. **Pull cart:** none. **Trail fee:** none.
Reservation policy: no. **Winter condition:** open. **Terrain:** flat.
Tees: grass. **Temporary greens:** no. **Services:** limited services provided.
Comments: Short course maintained for patient use. No outside play allowed.
The golf course is surrounded by trees, which come into play on several of the
holes. The golf course has a driving range net in which to practice in.

Directions: from I-5 take the City Center
exit and travel west. Turn right on East
Stewart Parkway to the golf course.

Course Yardage & Par:
M-2374 yards, par 35.
W-2374 yards, par 35.

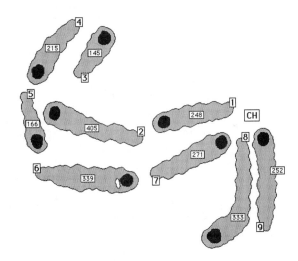

Round Lake Golf Course (public)
4000 Round Lake Road; Klamath Falls, OR 97601; (503) 884-2520
Manager: Ken Meyer. 9 hole executive course.
Rating/Slope: the golf course is not rated. **Course record:** 25.
Greens fee: $10/$6 all week long; student & Sr. rates; no credit cards.
Power cart: none available. **Pull cart:** $1. **Trail fee:** not allowed.
Reservation policy: no. **Winter condition:** golf course is closed from snowfall
to March or April depending on the weather. **Terrain:** flat. **Tees:** grass.
Temporary greens: no. **Services:** club rentals, restaurant, small pro shop, RV
parking. **Comments:** the golf course offers discount greens fee rates for people
who are staying at the RV park. The course has some trees but is fairly wide open.

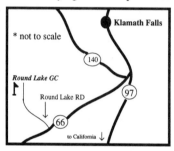

Directions: from Hwy 97 take Hwy 66
(Ashland Hwy) to Round Lake Road.
The golf course is located approximately
3.5 miles up Round Lake Road. The golf
course will be located on your right hand
side. Look for signs marking your way to
the course.

Course Yardage & Par:
M-1554 yards, par 29.
W-1554 yards, par 29.

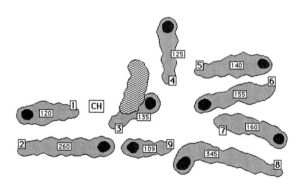

Sah-Hah-Lee Golf Course & Driving Range (public)

17104 SE 130th Ave; Clackamas, OR 97015; (503) 655-9249, 655-3215 (range)
Pro: Don Otto, PGA. 18 hole par 3 course, lighted & covered range.
Rating/Slope: the golf course is not rated. **Course record:** 50.
Greens fee: W/D $12/$7; W/E $13/$8; Jr. & Sr. rates weekdays only, $11/$6.
Power cart: none. **Pull cart:** $2/$1. **Trail fee:** not allowed.
Reservation policy: yes, taken for the weekend, please call in advance..
Winter condition: open, damp. **Terrain:** flat. **Tees:** grass & mats.
Temporary greens: no. **Services:** club rentals, lessons, snack bar, beer,
limited pro shop, driving range. **Comments:** great par 3 layout. You will use
every iron in your bag. Excellent driving range and practice facility.

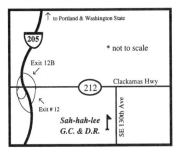

Directions: from I-205 northbound &
southbound exit at Hwy 212 going
eastbound. Proceed to SE 130th Ave
and head southbound to the golf course.
Look for signs to the golf course.

Course Yardage & Par:
M-2426 yards, par 54.
W-2426 yards, par 54.

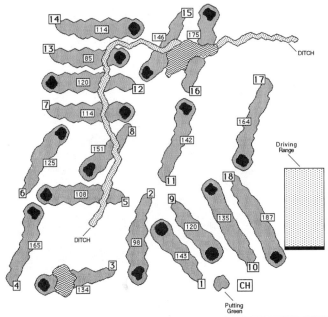

Saint Helens Golf Course (public)

57246 Hazen Road; Warren, OR 97053; (503) 397-0358
Pro: Jeff Stirling, PGA. 9 hole course, dual tees for 18 holes.
Rating/Slope: M 68.0/116; W 70.3/108. **Course record:** 65.
Greens fee: Mon.-Thurs. $13/$7; Fri.-Sun. $17/$9; Sr. rates; no credit cards.
Power cart: $18/$9. **Pull cart:** $2. **Trail fee:** $8/$4.
Reservation policy: yes. **Winter condition:** open.
Terrain: flat, some hills. **Tees:** grass. **Temporary greens:** no.
Services: club rentals, snack bar, beer, wine, pro shop, practice range.
Comments: Course has challenging greens and lush fairways. The golf course
can always be found in great shape. Not a bad walking golf course.

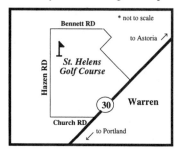

Directions: from Hwy 30 go west on
Church Road for 1.5 miles. At Hazen
Road turn right. The golf course is located
.5 miles ahead on your right hand side.
Note: Look for signs marking your way to
the golf course from the Hwy.

Course Yardage & Par:
M-2934 yards, par 36.
W-2663 yards, par 36.
Dual Tees 18 holes:
M-6003 yards, par 71.
W-5503 yards, par 73.

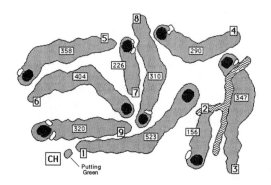

Salem Golf Club (semi-private)

2025 Golf Course Road S; Salem, OR 97302; (503) 363-6652
Pros: Paul Sundin, PGA, Danny Moore, PGA. 18 hole course.
Rating/Slope: C 69.6/118; M 68.0/114; W 72.9/119. **Course record:** 64.
Greens fee: $28/$15. **Power cart:** $20/$10. **Pull cart:** $1. **Trail fee:** $20/$10.
Reservation policy: call ahead for play after mens and womens clubs daily.
Winter condition: open. **Terrain:** flat, some hills. **Tees:** grass. **Temporary
greens:** no. **Services:** club rentals, lessons, snack bar, restaurant, beer, wine,
pro shop. **Comments:** Club established in 1928. Beautiful old colonial style
clubhouse in a picturesque setting. Course has a dress code. Visitors are
welcome with restricted tee times. Well maintained course. Worth a trip.

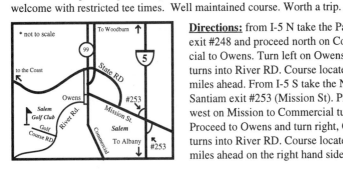

Directions: from I-5 N take the Parkway
exit #248 and proceed north on Commercial to Owens. Turn left on Owens which
turns into River RD. Course located 1.9
miles ahead. From I-5 S take the North
Santiam exit #253 (Mission St). Proceed
west on Mission to Commercial turn left.
Proceed to Owens and turn right, Owens
turns into River RD. Course located 1.9
miles ahead on the right hand side.

<u>**Course Yardage & Par:**</u>
C-6183 yards, par 72; M-5835 yards, par 72; W-5384 yards, par 72.

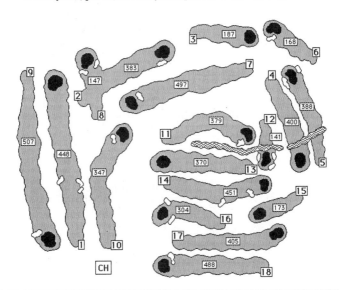

Salemtowne Golf Club (private)

2900 Oakcrest Drive NW; Salem, OR 97304; (503) 362-2215
Superintendent: Gary Schafer. 9 hole course.
Rating/Slope: C 55.9/82; M 55/79; W 58.5/86. **Course record:** 25.
Greens fee: private club, members and guests only.
Power cart: none. **Pull cart:** none. **Trail fee:** not charge.
Reservation policy: not taken. **Winter condition:** open, dry.
Terrain: flat, some hills. **Tees:** grass. **Temporary greens:** no.
Services: full service private club. **Comments:** The golf course is well manicured
with excellent greens. The golf course sports many greenside bunkers that will
challenge any level of golfer. The course is fairly flat and easy to walk.

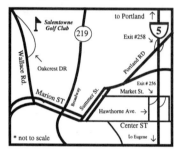

Directions: from I-5 take exit #256
(Market St. Silverton). West on Market
for 1.6 miles to Summer St. Turn left on
Summer and proceed .5 miles to Marion
St. Turn right. As you approach the
bridge stay right and follow signs for
Edgewater St. Dayton (Hwy 221).
Proceed for 3.4 miles to Oakcrest Dr.
Turn right. The pro shop will be on your
left hand side.

Course Yardage & Par:
M-1690 yards, par 30.
W-1657 yards, par 32.

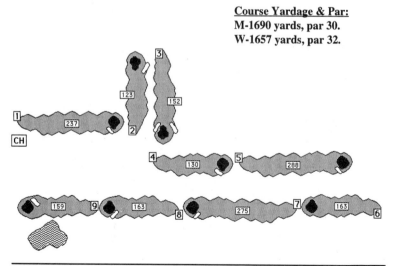

Salishan Golf Links (resort course)

Salishan Lodge; PO Box 118; Gleneden Beach, OR 97388; (503) 764-3632
Pro: Grant Rogers, PGA. 18 hole course, driving range.
Rating/Slope: C 72.1/128; M 71.1/126; W 73.6/127. **Course record:** 66.
Greens fee: $40/$25 lower rates for lodge guests; M/C, VISA, AMEX.
Power cart: $26/$15. **Pull cart:** $5/$3. **Trail fee:** personal carts not allowed.
Reservation policy: yes, please call up to 2 weeks in advance for tee times.
Winter condition: open, damp. **Terrain:** flat, some hills. **Tees:** grass.
Temporary greens: no. **Services:** club rentals, lessons, restaurant, beer,
wine, pro shop, driving range. **Comments:** Course was selected as one of the
top resort courses in America by Golf Digest in 1992. Excellent golfing facility.
Note: the course will be going through some reconstruction phases in the winter.

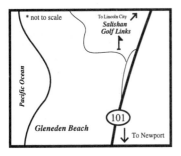

Directions: from I-5 take Ocean Beaches
Hwy to Hwy 101. The golf course is
located just south of Lincoln City in the
town of Gleneden Beach on the west side
of Hwy 101. Look for signs marking your
turn to the golf course.

Course Yardage & Par:
C-6439 yards, par 72.
M-6246 yards, par 72.
W-5693 yards, par 73.

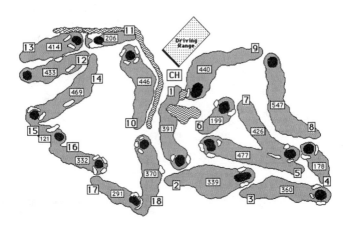

Sandelie Golf (public)

28333 SW Mountain Road; West Linn, OR 97068; (503) 655-1461
Owners: Bill & Jan Kaiser. 27 hole course.
Rating/Slope: M 66.6/99; W 72.0/109. **Course record:** 66.
Greens fee: W/D $16/$8; W/E $18/$9; Sr. rates on W/D's; no credit cards.
Power cart: power carts are not available. **Pull cart:** $2.
Reservation policy: call in advance for times. **Winter condition:** open.
Terrain: flat. **Tees:** grass. **Temporary greens:** no. **Services:** club rentals,
snacks, small pro shop. **Comments:** Beautiful course set back in the country
among rolling hills and tree lined fairways. The course does have some water
that the golfer will have to contend with other than that its fairly wide open.

Directions: from I-205 N&S take exit #3
(Stafford Road). Travel west on Stafford
Road for .8 miles to SW Mountain Road.
Turn left. The golf course is located 3.3
miles ahead on your right.

Course Yardage & Par:
M-5894 yards, par 70.
W-5406 yards, par 72.

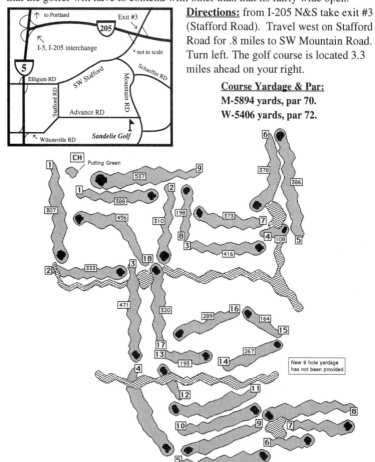

Sandpines Golf Resort (public resort)

1201 35th Street; Florence, OR 97439; (503) 997-1940, (800) 917-4653
Pro: Jim Skaugstad, PGA. 18 hole course. Course record: 68.
Rating/Slope: T 74.0/129; C 71.7/125; M 69.5/120; W 65.8/111.
Greens fee: $50/$30; Jr. rates. **Power cart:** $26/$18. **Pull cart:** $4/$2.
Trail fee: not allowed. **Reservation policy:** 14 days in advance.
Winter condition: dry. **Terrain:** flat, some hills. **Tees:** grass.
Temporary greens: no. **Services:** club rentals, lessons, snack bar, beer,
pro shop, driving range. **Comments:** a new Rees Jones design, this course is
built on the Oregon dunes with 6 water holes, 6 treed holes, and 6 dune holes.
When visiting the Oregon coast this new course is worth a special trip.

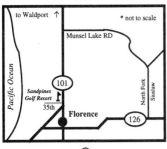

Directions: From Highway 101 turn
west on 35th street to the golf course.
The course is located in the north city
limits. Look for signs marking your
way to the golf course.

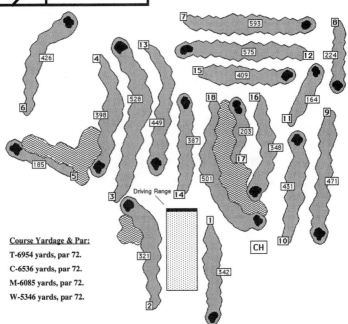

Course Yardage & Par:
T-6954 yards, par 72.
C-6536 yards, par 72.
M-6085 yards, par 72.
W-5346 yards, par 72.

Sandstrip Golf Course (public)
11875 Orr's Corner Road; Dallas, OR 97338; (503) 623-6832
Pro: Bruce Perisho, PGA. 9 hole executive course, driving range.
Rating/Slope: M 58.2/91. **Course record:** 55/26.
Greens fee: $13/$7; Jr. & Sr. rates. **Power cart:** $14/$7. **Pull cart:** $1.
Trail fee: $7/$3.50. **Reservation policy:** yes, please call ahead.
Winter condition: open, dry. **Terrain:** flat, some hills. **Tees:** grass.
Temporary greens: N/A. **Services:** club rentals, lessons, pro shop, driving range.
Comments: Ponds and bunkers come into play on several holes. Excellent
driving range to practice on. The golf course is well maintained and greens
generally putt true. Good golf course to stop at if you are in the area.

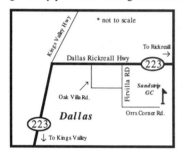

Directions: from Hwy 22 exit southbound
on Hwy 99 W for 1.7 miles to Orr's
Corner Road. Turn west. The golf course
is located 3 miles ahead on your left hand
side of the road. Look for signs marking
your way to the golf course.

Course Yardage & Par:
M-2031 yards, par 31.
W-2031 yards, par 31.

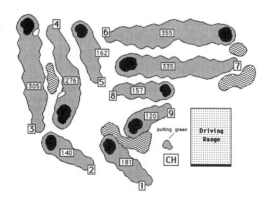

Santiam Golf Club (public)

off of Hwy 22; PO Box 447; Stayton, OR 97383; (503) 769-3485
Pro: Jack Coppedge, PGA. 18 hole course, driving range.
Rating/Slope: C 70.4/115; M 69.3/114; W 72.2/122. Course record: 63.
Greens fee: $22/$13; no credit cards; senior rates on Friday, $18/$13.
Power cart: $20/$11. Pull cart: $2. Trail fee: $10 for persoanl carts.
Reservation policy: yes, weekends, holidays. Winter condition: dry.
Terrain: flat. Tees: grass. Temporary greens: occasionally (but very seldom).
Services: club rentals, lessons, snack bar, restaurant, lounge, beer, wine,
liquor, driving range. Comments: Course is a good test of golf with lots
of trees, water and creeks challenge any golfer. Good walking course.

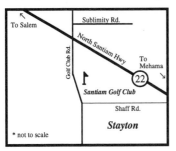

Directions: from I-5 take the Stayton exit.
Travel approximately 12 miles east on
Hwy 22 to the golf course. The golf course
is located on the south side of the Hwy 22.
Note: be sure to look for the golf course
from the Hwy marking your turn to the
clubhouse.

Course Yardage & Par:
C-6385 yards. par 72.
M-6155 yards, par 72.
W-5697 yards, par 75.

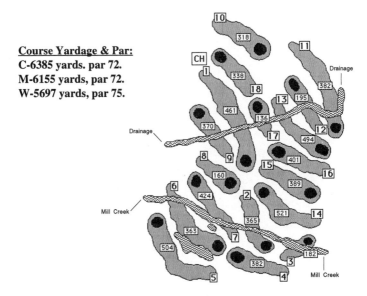

Seaside Golf Course (public)
451 Avenue U; Seaside, OR 97138; (503) 738-5261
Manager/Pro: Wayne Fulmer. 9 hole course.
Rating/Slope: M 64.9/104; W 69.6/106. **Course record:** 27.
Greens fee: W/D $16/$8; W/E $18/$9; no credit cards.
Power cart: $20/$10. **Pull cart:** $3/$1.50. **Trail fee:** $5.
Reservation policy: not required. **Winter condition:** damp. **Terrain:** flat.
Tees: grass. **Temporary greens:** yes, only in winter. **Services:** club rentals,
snack bar, restaurant, lounge, beer, wine, liquor, pro shop, putting green.
Comments: easy to walk and friendly. Course located on the fantastic Oregon
coast. The Necamicum River runs through the whole golf course and is a factor.

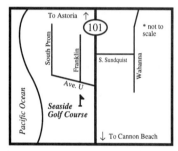

Directions: from Hwy 101 turn west on
Ave U. The golf course will be located on
your left hand side. (The golf course is
located in the south end of Seaside). The
golf course can be seen from Hwy 101.

Course Yardage & Par:
M-2593 yards, par 35.
W-2593 yards, par 35.

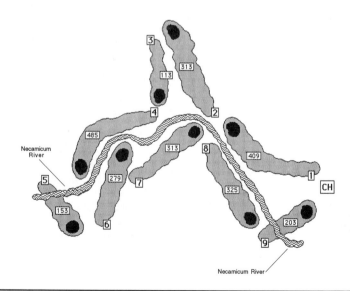

Senior Estates Golf & Country Club (private)
1776 Country Club Dr; Woodburn, OR 97071; (503) 981-0189
Pro: Jim White, PGA. 18 hole course, putting green.
Rating/Slope: M 65.6/101; W 67.9/103. **Course record:** 66.
Greens fee: private club members & guests only; reciprocates; M/C, VISA.
Power cart: private club. **Pull cart:** private club. **Trail fee:** not allowed.
Reservation policy: no, private club members & guests only.
Winter condition: open, wet. **Terrain:** flat. **Tees:** grass.
Temporary greens: yes. **Services:** club rentals, lessons, restaurant, pro shop.
Comments: Easy walking golf course. Course is well taken care of. Very
popular senior course with many retirement homes around the layout.

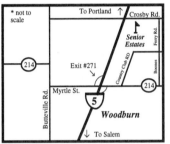

Directions: from Hwy 99 eastbound travel
north on Newberg Hwy. Travel 2.1 miles
to Country Club Dr. Turn right. Travel .3
miles to the golf course entrance on your
right. From I-5 take the Woodburn exit.
Travel east on Newberg Hwy for .5 miles to
Country Club Dr. Turn left. Follow for .3
miles to the course entrance on your right.

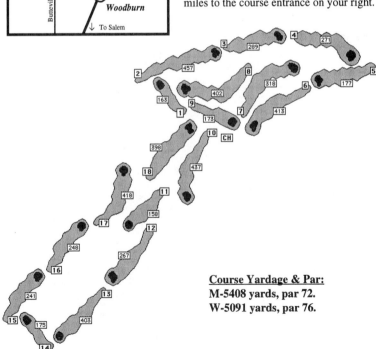

Course Yardage & Par:
M-5408 yards, par 72.
W-5091 yards, par 76.

Shadow Butte Municipal Golf Course (public)

Butler Boulevard; Box 684; Ontario, OR 97914; (503) 889-9022
Pro: Brooks Farnsworth. 18 hole course, driving range.
Rating/Slope: C 70.4/112; M 69.3/110; W 73.3/120. **Course record:** 64.
Greens fee: $10.50/$8.50; M/C, VISA. Special rates on Mondays $9 all day.
Power cart: $15/$7.50. **Pull cart:** $3/$2. **Trail fee:** $5.
Reservation policy: no. **Winter condition:** closed Nov. 15th to Feb. 15th.
Terrain: flat, some hills. **Tees:** grass. **Temporary greens:** N/A.
Services: club rentals, lessons, snack bar, lounge, beer, wine, liquor, pro shop,
lockers, showers, driving range. **Comments:** Course is kept in excellent
condition during the peak summer season. Easy walking golf course.

Directions: from I-84 take exit #376 and
proceed west on Idaho. Turn left on 9th
and proceed to 4th Ave. At 4th Ave turn
right to Cairo Blvd. Turn left on Cairo
Blvd. Proceed to Butler and turn right on
Butler. Follow to Golf Course Road and
turn right to the golf course. The golf
course is located next to the airport on
the southwest edge of the city.

Course Yardage & Par:
C-6847 yards, par 72.
M-6542 yards, par 72.
W-5727 yards, par 74.

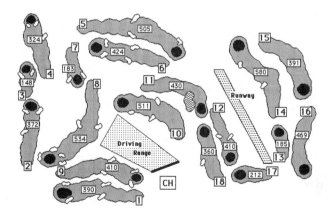

Shadow Hills Country Club (private)
92512 River Road; Junction City, OR 97448; (503) 998-8441
Pro: Mark Keating, PGA. 18 hole course, driving range.
Rating/Slope: C 71.9/128; M 70.8/125; W 71.0/118. **Course record:** 61.
Greens fee: private, members & guests only, reciprocates; M/C, VISA.
Power cart: private club. **Pull cart:** private club. **Trail fee:** not allowed.
Reservation policy: reciprocates call 2 days in advance. **Winter condition:**
open. **Terrain:** flat. **Tees:** grass. **Temporary greens:** no. **Services:** lessons,
restaurant, lounge, beer, wine, liquor, pro shop, showers, driving range.
Comments: Course is noted for the lush fairways and some of the best greens in
Oregon. The course sports a great deal of water and many greenside bunkers.

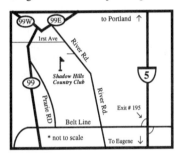

Directions: from I-5 take exit #195 and
travel west on Belt Line to River Road.
Travel north on River Road. The golf
course is 10 minutes from here. From
Hwy 99 travel east on River Road to the
golf course.

Course Yardage & Par:
C-6692 yards, par 72.
M-6453 yards, par 72.
M-5512 yards, par 72.
W-5512 yards, par 73.

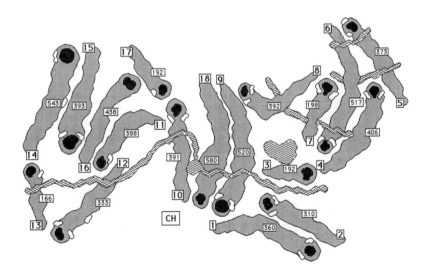

Shield Crest Golf Course (public)
3151 Shield Crest Drive; Klamath Falls, OR 97603; (503) 884-1493
Pro: Tom Schenke. 18 hole course, driving range.
Rating/Slope: C 72.1/122; M 70.6/120; W 73.4/118. **Course record:** 65.
Greens fee: W/D $20/$12; W/E $22/$15; (Sr. rates M-Thur); M/C, VISA.
Power cart: $18/$10. **Pull cart:** $2. **Trail fee:** not allowed.
Reservation policy: yes, 3 days in advance. **Winter condition:** open.
Terrain: flat, some hills. **Tees:** grass. **Temporary greens:** yes (at times).
Services: club rentals, lessons, restaurant, lounge, beer, wine, liquor, pro shop,
driving range. **Comments:** Water hazards and undulating greens make
this well kept course a challenge. Greens can be very difficult to read at times.

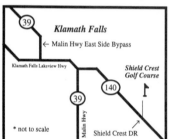

Directions: the golf course is located on
the southeast side of town. If you are
coming from the north on Hwy 97 take
the Alarenda Bypass and proceed through
town to Hwy 140. At Hwy 140 go east
toward Lakeview to the golf course. From
Hwy 140 go eastbound to Lakeview. The
golf course is located 1 mile beyond
Merrill, Lakeview Junction.

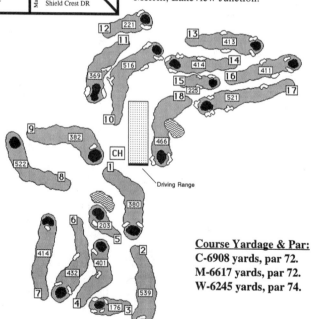

Course Yardage & Par:
C-6908 yards, par 72.
M-6617 yards, par 72.
W-6245 yards, par 74.

Spring Hill Country Club (private)

155 Country Club Lane; Albany, OR 97321; (503) 928-5454
Pro: Bill Raschko, PGA. 18 hole course.
Rating/Slope: C 71.1/119; M 69.7/115; W 71.7/117. **Course record:** 64.
Greens fee: private club members & guests only; reciprocates; no credit cards.
Power cart: private club. **Pull cart:** private club. **Trail fee:** private club.
Reservation policy: yes, 1 week in advance. **Winter condition:** open, damp.
Terrain: flat, some hills. **Tees:** grass. **Temporary greens:** yes. **Services:** club
rentals, lessons, restaurant, lounge, beer, wine, liquor, pro shop, lockers, showers,
driving range. **Comments:** Course has many mature trees that come into play on
several holes. Excellent greens and lush fairways are the trademark of this club.

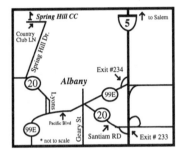

Directions: from I-5 N&S take exit #233
(Santiam Hwy 20) and go west to Main St
and turn right on Main. Proceed then to
1rst Ave and turn left (one way). Proceed
to Lyons and turn right. Proceed over
the bridge and take your first right on
Springhill Dr. Proceed to the Country
Club Lane turn left and proceed to the
golf course.

Course Yardage & Par:
C-6432 yards, par 72.
M-6145 yards, par 72.
W-5461 yards, par 73.

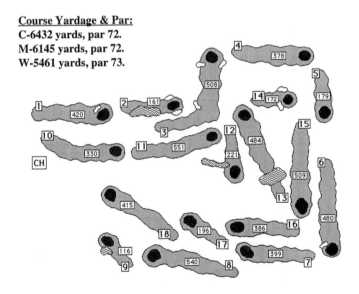

Springfield Country Club (private)

90333 Sunderman Road; Springfield, OR 97478; (503) 747-2517
Pro: Ron Wells, PGA. 18 hole course, driving range.
Rating/Slope: C 70.7/123; M 69.1/118; W 74.4/125. **Course record:** 63.
Greens fee: private club, members & guests only.
Power cart: private club. **Pull cart:** private club. **Trail fee:** private club.
Reservation policy: yes, 1 day in advance. **Winter condition:** open, damp.
Terrain: relatively hilly. **Tees:** grass. **Temporary greens:** yes.
Services: club rentals, lessons, restaurant, lounge, beer, wine, pro shop, lockers,
showers, driving range. **Comments:** Golf course plays longer than the yardage
indicates. Tough greens and several ponds make this golf course a challenge.

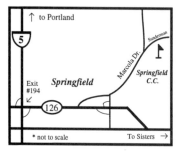

Directions: from I-5 N&S take exit
194 (Hwy 126) and go eastbound to
the 2nd exit (42nd). Turn left on 42nd
and proceed northbound to Marcola.
Turn right on Marcola and proceed to
Sunderman. At Sunderman turn right
to the golf course.

Course Yardage & Par:
C-6182 yards, par 71.
M-5912 yards, par 71.
W-5592 yards, par 73.

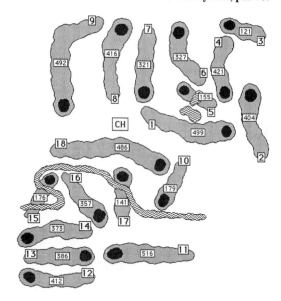

Springwater Golf Course (public)

25230 S Wallens Road; Estacada, OR 97023; (503) 630-4586
Owners: Pat & Vickie O'Meara. 9 hole course, dual tees for 18 holes.
Rating/Slope: M 67.7/102; W 72.8/116. **Course record: 32.**
Greens fee: W/D $14/$7; W/E & Hol. $18/$9; Sr. & Jr. rates M-F; no CC.
Power Cart: $15/$8. **Pull Cart:** $1. **Trail fee:** $2.50 for 9 holes.
Reservation policy: yes, summers only 3-5 days in advance.
Winter condition: open, dry. **Terrain:** relatively hilly. **Tees:** grass.
Temporary greens: no. **Services:** club rentals, snack bar, beer, wine, pro shop.
Comments: The golf course is noted for being very playable during the winter
months. Two sets of tees will offer a different look for 18 holes.

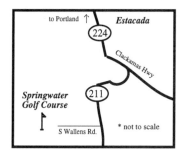

Directions: from Hwy 224 exit toward
Springwater in Estacada onto Hwy 211.
From Hwy 211 take Wallens Road all the
way up to road to the dead end where the
course is located. The golf course is
located 3 miles south of Estacada.

Course Yardage & Par:
M-3003 yards, par 36.
W-2479 yards, par 36.
Dual tees 18 holes:
M-6204 yards, par 72.
W-5355 yards, par 73.

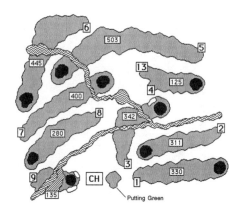

Stewart Meadows (public)

1801 South Holly Street; Medford, OR 97501; (503) 770-6554.
Pro: Dan Coughlin. 9 hole course, putting green.
Rating/Slope: M 67.6/115; W 68.2/115. **Course record:** 69.
Greens fee: $18/$10; Jr. rates, Sr. rates Thursday's only $10/$5.
Power cart: $9/$5 per person. **Pull cart:** $2/$1. **Trail fee:** not available.
Reservation policy: call in advance for a tee time. **Winter condition:** open,
weather permitting. **Terrain:** flat. **Tees:** grass. **Services:** club rentals, lessons,
snack bar, beer, wine, pro shop, driving range. **Comments:** A new course
beautifully mounded and landscaped. Ponds, bunkers,and a creek makes for
a challenging 9 holes of golf. The golf course opened in July of 1994.

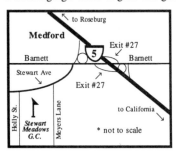

Directions: From I-5 N&S take
the Barnett Street exit to South Medford.
Cross Barnett Street to Stewart Avenue.
Proceed until you reach Holly Street.
Turn left on Holly Street. The golf course
is located on the left hand side of Holly
Street. Look for signs to the golf course.

Course Yardage & Par:
C-3000 yards, par 36.
M-2858 yards, par 36.
W-2580 yards, par 36.

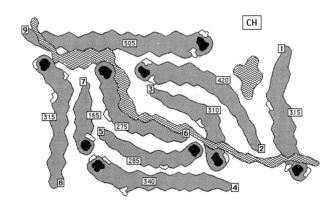

Stewart Park Golf Course (public)

1005 Stewart Parkway; Roseburg, OR 97470; (503) 672-4592
Manager: Jim Wakeman. 9 hole course, driving range.
Rating/Slope: M 68.7/112; W 73.5/118. **Course record:** 64.
Greens fee: W/D $13/$7.50; W/E $15/$9.50; Sr. rates (weekdays); M/C, VISA.
Power cart: $16/$9. **Pull cart:** $2. **Trail fee:** N/A.
Reservation policy: yes, call 1 week in advance. **Winter condition:** open, dry.
Terrain: flat, some hills. **Tees:** grass. **Temporary greens:** no.
Services: club rentals, snack bar, beer, wine, pro shop, driving range.
Comments: Monthly discounted rates available. Water hazards, bunkers and
newly planted trees make this course a challenge. Great nine hole tract.

Directions: from I-5 take the City
Center exit (#124) and travel west.
Turn right on Stewart Parkway to the
golf course. The golf course will be
located on your right hand side.

Course Yardage & Par:
M-2909 yards, par 35.
W-2835 yards, par 37.

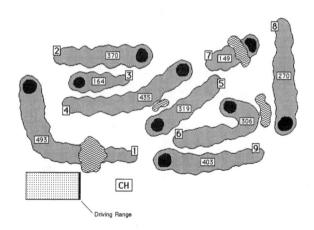

Stoneridge Golf Course (public)

1523 Satellite Drive; Medford, OR 97504; (503) 830-GOLF
Manager: Jim Cochran. 18 hole course, driving range.
Rating/Slope: to be determined upon opening. **Course record:** N/A
Greens fee: W/D $22/$12; W/E $25/$15; ask for special rates.
Power cart: $18/$10. **Pull cart:** $3/$2. **Trail fee:** personal carts not allowed.
Reservation policy: public call 1 week in advance for tee times.
Winter condition: course is open, damp. **Terrain:** flat, some moderate hills.
Tees: grass. **Temporary greens:** not in use. **Services:** club rentals, lessons, snack bar, beer, wine, pro shop, driving range. **Comments:** beautiful championship course. Elevated tees, excellent greens, lots of character, every hole on this new course is unique. This course is due to open in early June of 1995.

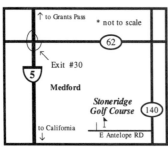

Directions: from I-5 N&S take exit #30. Proceed eastbound on Hwy 62. Proceed for 6 miles to Hwy 140 and turn right. Proceed 3 miles to East Antelope Road. turn right. Proceed 1/4 mile to the golf course entrance.

Course Yardage & Par:
C-6965 yards, par 72.
M-6552 yards, par 72.
S-6064 yards, par 72.
W-5151 yards, par 72.

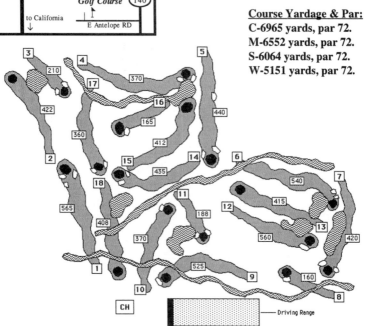

Summerfield Golf & Country Club (semi-private)
10650 SW Summerfield Drive; Tigard, OR 97224; (503) 620-1200
Pro: Bill Houston, PGA. 9 hole course, dual tees for 18 holes.
Rating/Slope: M 61.4/96; W 65.0/103. Course record: 29.
Greens fee: W/D $20/$10; W/E $20/$10; no credit cards.
Power cart: $18/$9. **Pull cart:** $2. **Trail fee:** not allowed.
Reservation policy: public call ahead, course open after mens & ladies
club play. **Winter condition:** open. **Terrain:** flat, some hills.
Tees: grass. **Temporary greens:** yes. **Services:** pro shop, lessons.
Comments: Course is situated among beautiful homes and club house.
The golf course is moderately flat so it is very easy to walk.

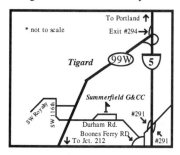

Directions: from I-5 take the Hwy 99
W exit. Travel south through King City.
Turn left on SW Durham. Take the first
left at the light on SW Summerfield Dr.
Stay right for .5 miles to the golf course
which will be located on your right.

Course Yardage & Par:
M-2320 yards, par 33.
W-2231 yards, par 33.
Dual Tees 18 holes:
M-4673 yards, par 66.
W-4452 yards, par 66.

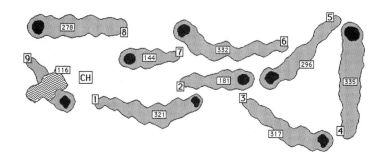

Sunriver Lodge & Resort (north course-public) _woodlands_
PO Box 3609; Sunriver, OR 97707; (503) 593-1221, (800) 962-1769
Director of Golf Operations: to be determined. 18 hole course.
Rating/Slope: C 73.0/131; M 70.2/125; W 70.3/118. **Course record:** 63.
Greens fee: $59/$20; lower rates for guests & homeowners; M/C, VISA,
AMEX, DIS. **Power cart:** $28. **Pull cart:** $3/$1.50. **Trail fee:** not allowed.
Reservation policy: lodge guests through golf reservation number, public 7 days.
Winter condition: closed November 1st to April 9th. **Terrain:** flat, some hills.
Tees: grass. **Services:** club rentals, lessons, snack bar, beer, pro shop, driving
range, tennis, swimming, full resort facility. **Comments:** Course designed by
Robert Trent Jones II. Rated in _Golf Digest's_ top 25 resort courses in America.

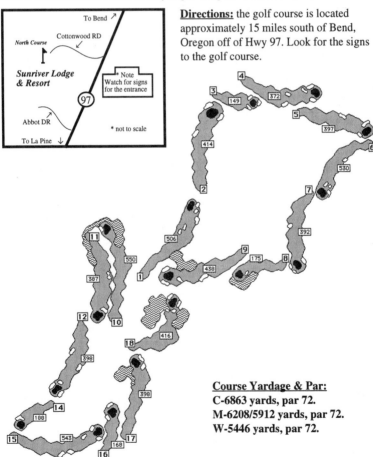

Directions: the golf course is located
approximately 15 miles south of Bend,
Oregon off of Hwy 97. Look for the signs
to the golf course.

Course Yardage & Par:
C-6863 yards, par 72.
M-6208/5912 yards, par 72.
W-5446 yards, par 72.

Sunriver Lodge & Resort (south course-public) *Meadows*

PO Box 3609; Sunriver, OR 97707; (503) 593-1221, (800) 962-1769
Director of Golf Operations: to be determined. **18 hole course.**
Rating/Slope: C 72.9/130; M 70.8/125; W 71.7/116. **Course record:** 64.
Greens fee: $49/$16; lower rates for guests & homeowners; M/C, VISA,
AMEX, DIS. **Power cart:** $28. **Pull cart:** $3/$1.50. **Trail fee:** not allowed.
Reservation policy: lodge guests at reservation time, public 7 days in advance.
Winter condition: closed November 30th to April 1st. **Terrain:** flat, some hills.
Tees: grass. **Services:** club rentals, lessons, snack bar, restaurant, lounge, beer,
wine, pro shop, driving range. **Comments:** Course wanders through lush meadows
and tree lined fairways. Fantastic views of Mt. Bachelor throughout the course.

Directions: the golf course is located
approximately 15 miles south of Bend,
Oregon off of Hwy 97. Look for signs
to the golf course.

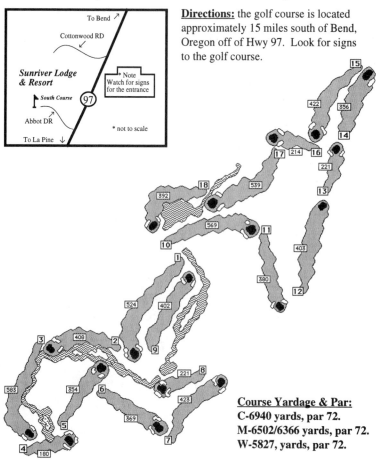

Course Yardage & Par:
C-6940 yards, par 72.
M-6502/6366 yards, par 72.
W-5827, yards, par 72.

Sunset Bay Golf Course (public)
11001 Cape Arago Hwy; Coos Bay, OR 97420; (503) 888-9301
Pro: none. 9 hole course, dual tees for 18 holes.
Rating/Slope: M 68.0/ no slope; W 69.7/ no slope. **Course record:** 31.
Greens fee: W/D $14/$8; W/E $15/$9; Jr. rates; M/C, VISA.
Power cart: $17/$9. **Pull cart:** $2/$1. **Trail fee:** not allowed.
Reservation policy: no. **Winter condition:** open, dry. **Terrain:** flat, some hills.
Tees: grass. **Temporary greens:** N/A. **Services:** club rentals, snack bar,
pro shop. **Comments:** Course opened in 1969, and was designed by John
Zoller, winner of the 1990 Ross Award for Golf Course architecture.
"One of the most interesting courses anywhere" Golf Oregon Magazine. The
golf course is planning to expand to 18 holes in the near future.

Directions: the golf course is located in
the Charleston Recreation Area, 12 miles
west of Coos Bay, it adjoins Sunset Bay
State Park. From Hwy 101 follow the
signs to Charleston, state parks, ocean
beaches, and the golf course. Look for
signs marking your way to the golf course.

Course Yardage & Par:
Yellow/Blue tees: 3020 yards, par 36.
White/Red tees: 2609 yards, par 36.
Dual tees 18 holes:
Yellow/Blue tees: 6055 yards, par 72.
White/Red tees: 5415 yards, par 72.

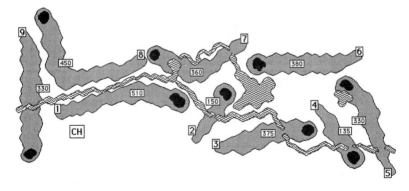

Sunset Grove Golf Club (public)

off of Hwy 47; Route 2 Box 406; Forest Grove, OR 97116; (503) 357-6044
Owner: Chip Abarno. 9 hole course, dual tees for 18 holes.
Rating/Slope: M 66.1/103; W 69.04 104. **Course record:** 63.
Greens fee: W/D $14/$7; W/E $16/$8; Jr. & Sr. rates (weekdays); M/C, VISA.
Power cart: $16/$8. **Pull cart:** $1.50. **Trail fee:** not allowed.
Reservation policy: yes, call for reservations, they advised them in summer.
Winter condition: open, dry. **Terrain:** flat, easy walking. **Tees:** grass.
Temporary greens: yes. **Services:** club rentals, snack bar, beer, wine, pro shop.
Comments: the golf course is very dry during the winter months. It's wide
open and plays to an intermediate level. The golf course is easy to walk.

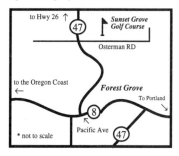

Directions: the golf course is located
between Banks and Forest Grove,
Oregon. From Portland take Hwy 26
west to Hwy 6, then cut off to Hwy 47
south. The golf course is located on
the east side of Hwy 47. Look for signs.

<u>**Course Yardage & Par:**</u>
M-2849 yards, par 36.
W-2715 yards, par 37.
<u>**Dual Tees 18 holes:**</u>
M-5564 yards, par72.
W-5430 yards, par74.

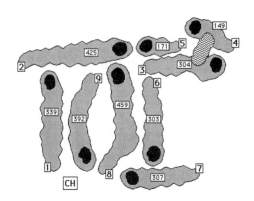

The Dalles Country Club (private)
4550 Hwy 30 West; The Dalles, OR 97058; (503) 296-5252
Pro: Bob Sproule, PGA. 9 hole course, dual tees for 18 holes.
Rating/Slope: M 69.4/120; W 73.6/118. **Course record:** 61.
Greens fee: private club members onlyor guest of a member; reciprocates.
Power cart: private club members only. **Pull cart:** private club.
Trail fee: not allowed. **Reservation policy:** private club.
Winter condition: open. **Terrain:** flat, some hills. **Tees:** grass.
Temporary greens: no. **Services:** snack bar, restaurant, lounge, beer, wine,
liquor, pro shop, lockers, showers. **Comments:** Course is ranked as one of the
best nine hole courses in Oregon by the National Golf Foundation. Good course.

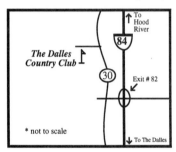

Directions: from I-84 take exit #82 to
Hwy 30. Go westbound on Hwy 30.
The golf course is located just west of
The Dalles Oregon off of Hwy 30.

Course Yardage & Par:
C-3060 yards, par 36.
W-2868 yards, par 37.
Dual Tees 18 holes:
M-6034 yards, par 71.
W-5810 yards, par 73.

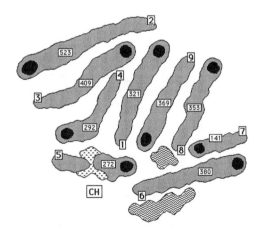

The OGA Members Course at Tukwila (public)

2990 Boones Ferry Road; Woodburn, OR 97071; (503) 981-6105
Pro: Chuck Siver, PGA. 18 hole course, driving range.
Rating/Slope: T 73.6/135; C 72.2/130; &0.6/126; W 73.2/126. **Record:** 67.
Greens fee: W/D $30/$16; W/E $35/$18. **Power cart:** $20/$10. **Pull cart:** $2.
Trail fee: not allowed. **Reservation policy:** call up to 5 days in advance.
Winter condition: open, weather permitting. **Terrain:** rolling hills. **Tees:** grass.
Services: club rentals, lessons, snack bar, beer, wine, pro shop, driving range.
Comments: This course has a unique double green on holes 9 and 18. Water comes into play on several holes, some holes offer a peek-a-boo view of Mount Hood. This course will be a trip worth anytime. Lower rates for OGA members.

Directions: From I-5 N&S take exit #271, Woodburn. Head eastbound for approximately .5 miles to Boones Ferry Road and turn left. The golf course is ahead on the right hand side of the road. Look for signs marking your way to the course.

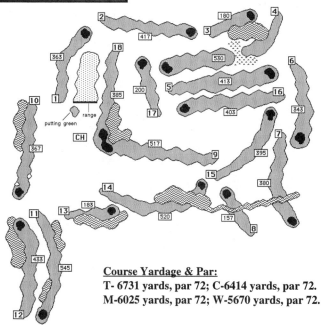

Course Yardage & Par:
T- 6731 yards, par 72; C-6414 yards, par 72.
M-6025 yards, par 72; W-5670 yards, par 72.

Tokatee Golf Club (public)

54947 McKenzie Hwy Blue River, OR 97413; PO Box 989 Eugene OR 97440
Pro: Mickey Sullivan, PGA. 18 hole course. (503) 822-3220, (800) 452-6376 OR
Rating/Slope: C 72.0/126; M 69.7/119; W 71.2/115. Course record: 65.
Greens fee: $30/$16; no credit cards. **Power cart:** $23/$14. **Pull cart:** $3/$2.
Trail fee: $10. **Reservation policy:** yes, call up to 30 days in advance.
Winter condition: closed from November 15th to February 1st. **Terrain:** walkable.
Tees: grass. **Temporary greens:** no. **Services:** club rentals, coffee shop, beer,
pro shop, driving range. **Comments:** the golf course has been rated in the top 25
of *Golf Digests* "America's Best Public Golf Courses" in 1984, 86, 88, 90 and also
in 1991. A very nice surprise in Oregon. This golf course is worth a special trip.

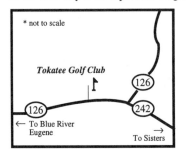

Directions: the golf course is located 47.5
miles east of Eugene, Oregon on Hwy 126
(near Blue River). From Hwy 126 the golf
course is located 7 miles east of the Blue
River exit. Look for signs marking your
way to the golf course.

Course Yardage & Par:
Blue tees: 6842 yards, par 72.
White tees: 6245 yards, par 72.
Red tees: 5651 yards, par 72.

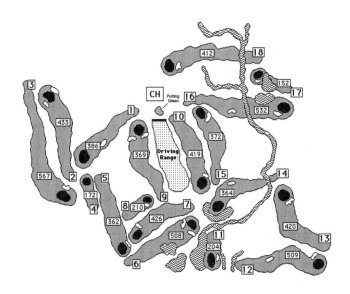

Top O'Scott Golf Course (public)

12000 SE Stevens Road; Portland, OR 97266; (503) 654-5050
Manager: Romaine D. Challis. 18 hole course.
Rating/Slope: M 63.9/99; W 62.3/96. **Course record:** 61.
Greens fee: W/D $14/$8; W/E $16/$9; Jr. & Sr. rates on weekdays; M/C, VISA.
Power cart: $18/$10. **Pull cart:** $1. **Trail fee:** $3, $1 for passengers.
Reservation policy: yes, weekends, holidays. **Winter condition:** open, damp.
Terrain: flat, some hills. **Tees:** grass. **Temporary greens:** yes.
Services: club rentals, vending machines. **Comments:** Tree lined fairways and tricky greens make this course a challenge. A ditch runs through most of the golf course and presents a challenge on many of the holes. Good golf course.

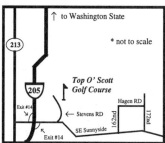

Directions: from I-205 southbound exit at Sunnyside Road and travel eastbound. Turn left on Kaiser Hospital, Stevens Road. The golf course is located across from the New Hope Church on Stevens Road. Look for signs marking your way to the golf course.

Course Yardage & Par:
M-5254 yards, par 69.
W-4766 yards, par 72.

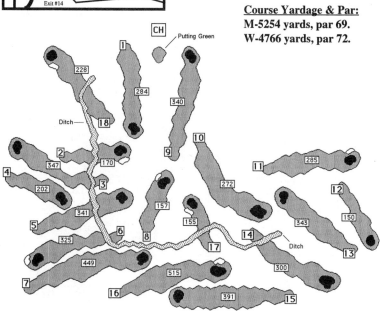

Trysting Tree Golf Club (public)

34028 Electric Road; Corvallis, OR 97333; (503) 752-3332
Pro: Sean Arey, PGA. 18 hole course. Course record: 65.
Rating/Slope: T 73.9/129; C 72.1/128; M 69.9/122; W 71.3/118.
Greens fee: $23/$13; Oregon College students $12/$7; Jr. rates; no credit cards.
Power cart: $22/$12. **Pull cart:** $2. **Trail fee:** $10.
Reservation policy: yes, 1 week in advance. **Winter condition:** open, dry.
Terrain: flat, some hills. **Tees:** grass. **Temporary greens:** no.
Services: club rentals, lessons, snack bar, pro shop, driving range.
Comments: Beautiful Scottish links style golf course with mounds and swales
throughout the golf course. Water and bunkers are the major factor at this course.

Directions: from I-5 N&S take the exit
for Hwy 34 westbound toward Corvallis.
Proceed 9 miles. Turn right on Electric
Road to the golf course. The golf course
is located on the north side of the road.
Look for signs marking your way to the
golf course.

Course Yardage & Par:
T-7014 yards, par 72.
C-6674 yards, par 72.
M-6216 yards, par 72.
W-5516 yards, par 72.

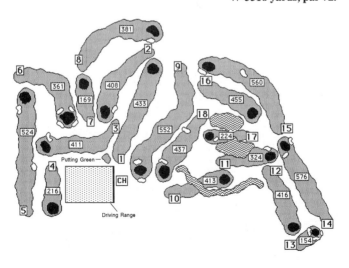

Tualatin Country Club (private)

9145 Tualatin Road; Tualatin, OR 97062; (503) 692-4620
Pro: John Peterson, PGA. 18 hole course.
Rating/Slope: C 72.1/133; M 69.8/125; W 71.2/120. **Course record:** 65.
Greens fee: private club members & guest only.
Power cart: private club. **Pull cart:** private club. **Trail fee:** members only.
Reservation policy: yes, weekends. **Winter condition:** open, dry.
Terrain: flat, some hills. **Tees:** grass. **Temporary greens:** no.
Services: club rentals, lessons, snack bar, beer, wine, clubhouse, pro shop.
Comments: flat, very easy walking course that has been recently renovated to be more challenging to it's members. Tree-lined fairways make this course tight.

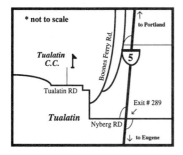

Directions: from I-5N take exit #289 (Tualatin). Turn left over the freeway. Take the first left on SW Nyberg, go .5 miles to Boones Ferry. Turn right. Proceed .3 miles to SW Tualatin. Turn left on SW Tualatin. Travel .4 miles to the front entrance, turn right to the course.

Course Yardage & Par:
C-6611 yards, par 72.
M-6054 yards, par 72.
W-5468 yards, par 72.

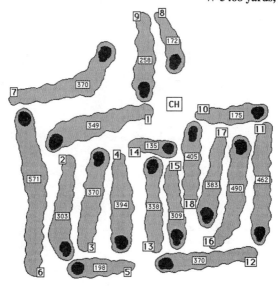

Umatilla Golf Course (public)
705 Willamette; Umatilla, OR 97882; (503) 922-3006
Pro: Jim Warner, PGA. 18 hole course.
Rating/Slope: M 68.9/113; W 72.5/119. **Course record:** 65.
Greens fee: W/D $14/$7; W/E $16/$8; Jr. rates; M/C, VISA.
Power cart: $20/$10. **Pull cart:** $1.50./$1 **Trail fee:** $5.
Reservation policy: no. **Winter condition:** open, dry. **Terrain:** flat.
Tees: grass. **Temporary greens:** N/A. **Services:** club rentals, lessons,
restaurant, lounge, beer, wine, liquor, pro shop, lodging at the motel.
Comments: a challenging 18 hole layout that offers every golfer a challenge.
The golf course is flat and very easy to walk. Great golf course for seniors.

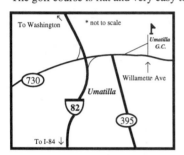

Directions: from I-84 E&W exit at
Irrigon/Umatilla. Proceed eastbound for
14.5 miles through Umatilla city center.
The golf course will be located 2 miles
ahead. There are well marked signs along
the way. The golf course is located at
Nendel's Resort.

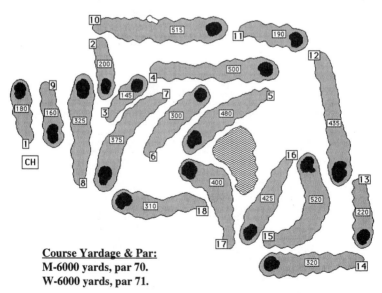

Course Yardage & Par:
M-6000 yards, par 70.
W-6000 yards, par 71.

Valley Golf Club (public)
345 Hines Boulevard, PO Box 96; Hines, OR 97882; (503) 573-6251
Manager: N/A. **9 hole course, dual tees for 18 holes.**
Rating/Slope: M 69.4/107; W 73.2/115. **Course record:** 33.
Greens fee: $15/$9 all week long; no credit cards.
Power cart: $18/$10. **Pull cart:** $1. **Trail fee:** $5.
Reservation policy: not necessary. **Winter condition:** open, dry.
Terrain: flat. **Tees:** grass. **Temporary greens:** yes.
Services: club rentals, snack bar, showers, pro shop.
Comments: Course is well conditioned and easy to walk. The golf course is
fairly long and can play tough when you stray from the fairway.

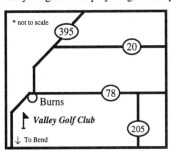

Directions: the golf course is located
between the intersections of Hwy 395
and Hwy 20, in the town of Hines
Oregon. The golf course is right off of
Hwy 395. Look for signs marking your
way to the golf course.

Course Yardage & Par:
M-3190 yards, par 36.
W-3190 yards, par 38.
Duals Tees 18 holes:
M-6405 yards, par 72.
W-6405 yards, par 72.

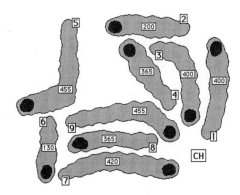

Vernonia Golf Club (public)
15961 Timber Road East; Vernonia, OR 97064; (503) 429-6811
Manager: Fred Fulmer III. 9 hole course, dual tees for 18 holes.
Rating/Slope: M 66.8/113; W 68.8/111. **Course record:** 63.
Greens fee: W/D $13/$7; W/E $15/$8; Jr. & Sr. rates (M-F); no credit cards.
Power cart: $20/$10. **Pull cart:** $2. **Trail fee:** $4. **Reservation policy:** yes,
weekends, holidays. **Winter condition:** open, dry. **Terrain:** flat, some hills.
Tees: grass. **Temporary greens:** N/A. **Services:** club rentals, lessons snack bar,
beer, wine, pro shop. **Comments:** course was established in 1928. The course is
situated in a very scenic, quiet, rural setting along the Nehalem River. It is located
45 minutes from downtown Portland. Course has dual tees for 18 hole play. Look
for Vernonia to be expanding to 18 holes in the near future.

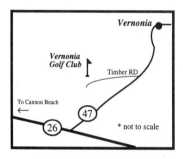

Directions: from Hwy 26 westbound
from Portland to Hwy 47 (Vernonia exit).
Proceed for 14 miles. Turn left on Timber
Road. Proceed for 1 mile. The golf course
will be located on your right hand side.

Course Yardage & Par:
M--2701 yards, par 35.
W-2547 yards, par 36.
Dual Tees 18 holes:
M-5536 yards, par 71.
W-5097 yards, par 72.

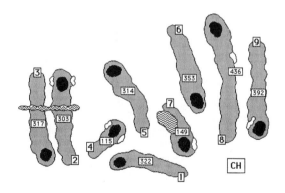

Veterans Administration Domiciliary Golf Course (private)

Domiciliary Golf Course; White City, OR 97503; (503) 826-2111
Golf Shop Director: Ron Riddle. 9 hole course
Rating/Slope: the golf course is not rated. **Course Record:** 29.
Greens fee: course is for patients and staff of the domiciliary. Play allowed for
outpatients along with their guests as long as they have proper paperwork.
Power Cart: no charge. **Pull Cart:** no charge. **Trail fee:** no charge.
Reservation policy: no. **Winter condition:** open. **Terrain:** flat.
Tees: grass. **Temporary greens:** no. **Services:** all services provided by the
Veterans Administration. **Comments:** Golf course is one of the finest
recreational standpoints of the White City Domiciliary Recreation Program.

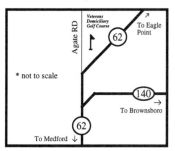

Directions: the golf course is located
northeast of Medford off of Hwy 62

Course Yardage & Par:
White tees: 2018 yards, par 33.
Blue tees: 2018 yards, par 33.

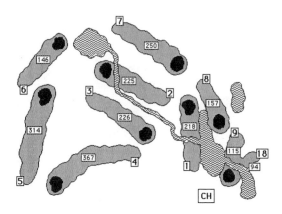

Waverley Country Club (private)

1100 SE Waverley Drive; Portland, OR 97222; (503) 654-9509
Pro: John Wells, PGA. 18 hole course. driving range
Rating/Slope: C 71.6/119; M 70.4/116; W 73.3/121. **Course record:** 65.
Greens fee: private club; members only; no outside play.
Power cart: private club; members only. **Pull cart:** members only.
Reservation policy: members only. **Winter condition:** dry. **Terrain:** flat, some
hills. **Tees:** grass. **Temporary greens:** yes (at times). **Services:** full service
private club, restaurant, pro shop, lounge, showers, driving range (members only).
Comments: Course is rich with tradition and character. One of the finest courses
in the state of Oregon. Host of many major tournaments throughout the years.

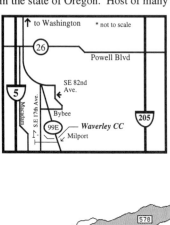

Directions: from Hwy 99E (McLoughlin
Blvd), take Hwy 224 exit and travel
westbound to 17th. Turn right (north).
Proceed to Waverly Drive. At Waverly
Drive turn left to the golf course.

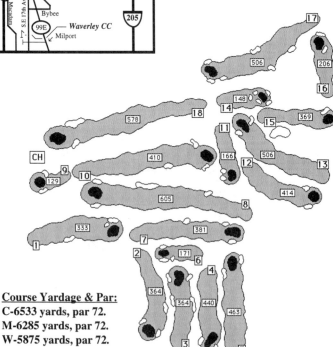

Course Yardage & Par:
C-6533 yards, par 72.
M-6285 yards, par 72.
W-5875 yards, par 72.

Widgi Creek Golf Club (semi-private)
18707 Century Drive; Bend, OR 97702; (503) 382-4449
Pro: Jeff Jarvis. 18 hole course, driving range. Course record: 69.
Rating/Slope: T 73.4/134; C 71.3/132; M 68.7/122; F 64.8/112.
Greens fee: W/D $37/$24; W/E $42/$28; winter rates; M/C, VISA.
Power cart: $13/$8 per person. **Pull cart:** $3/$2. **Trail fee:** not allowed.
Reservation policy: yes, public 7 days in advance, hotel guests with reservation.
Winter condition: closed in winter. **Terrain:** flat, some hills. **Tees:** grass.
Services: club rentals, lessons, snack bar, beer, wine, pro shop, lockers, showers,
driving range. **Comments:** championship course designed by Robert Muir Graves.
The course borders the Deschutes National Forest. A challenging, beautiful track.

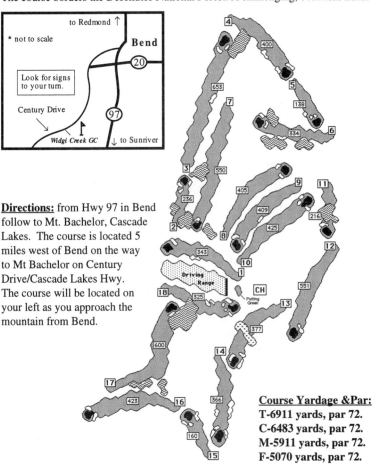

Directions: from Hwy 97 in Bend
follow to Mt. Bachelor, Cascade
Lakes. The course is located 5
miles west of Bend on the way
to Mt Bachelor on Century
Drive/Cascade Lakes Hwy.
The course will be located on
your left as you approach the
mountain from Bend.

Course Yardage &Par:
T-6911 yards, par 72.
C-6483 yards, par 72.
M-5911 yards, par 72.
F-5070 yards, par 72.

Wildwood Golf Course (public)

21281 NW Saint Helens Road; Portland, OR 97231; (503) 621-3402
Owners: Bill & Kay O'Meara. 9 hole course.
Rating/Slope: golf course is not rated. **Course record:** 33.
Greens fee: W/D $12/$6*; W/E$16/$8*. (*subject to change)
Power cart: $14/$7*. **Pull cart:** $2/$1*. **Trail fee:** $3*.
Reservation policy: call anytime. **Winter condition:** open, damp.
Terrain: flat, some hills. **Tees:** grass. **Temporary greens:** no.
Services: club rentals, lessons, pro shop, restaurant.
Comments: friendly family run course. This golf course sports three creeks
running through it. Great place to host a casual golf tournament or outing. Look
for Wildwood to be expanding to 18 holes in the near future. Good golf course.

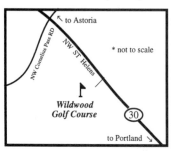

Directions: The golf course is located
right off of Hwy 30, 2 miles west of the
Cornelius Pass turnoff. The course will
be located on the west side of Hwy 30.

Course Yardage & Par:
M-2945 yards, par 36.
W-2725 yards, par 36.

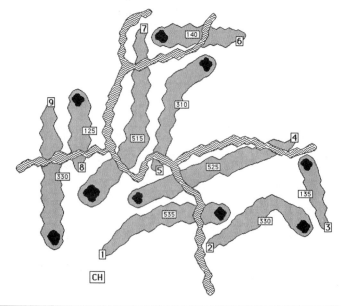

Willamette Valley Country Club (private)

900 Country Club Drive; Canby, OR 97013; (503) 266-2102
Pro: Pat Akins, PGA. 18 hole course, driving range.
Rating/Slope: C 74.2/132; M 71.2/131; W 71.8/124. **Course record:** 65.
Greens fee: private; reciprocates with other private clubs.
Power cart: private club. **Pull cart:** private. **Trail fee:** private club.
Reservation policy: yes. **Winter condition:** open, dry. **Terrain:** flat.
Tees: grass. **Temporary greens:** yes. **Services:** pro shop, restaurant, lounge,
showers, driving range. **Comments:** Course has tree lined fairways and well
conditioned greens. Excellent private facility. Almost all of the greens are
guarded by greenside bunkers. The course can play very tight at times.

Directions: From Hwy 99E turn westbound on Territorial Rd. Proceed to Maple
and turn right. Proceed to the golf course
entrance which will be on your right.

Course Yardage & Par:
C-7008 yards, par 72.
M-6401 yards, par 72.
W-5509 yards, par 72.

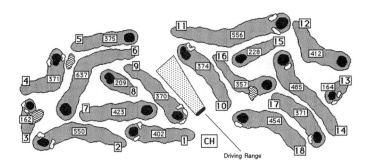

Willow Creek Country Club (semi-private)
State Route 74; PO Box 64; Heppner, OR 97836; (503) 676-5437
Pro: none. 9 hole executive course, dual tees for 18 holes.
Rating/Slope: M 56.7/83; W 59.2/85. **Course record:** 26.
Greens fee: $8/$5 all week long; no credit cards.
Power cart: none available. **Pull cart:** $2. **Trail fee:** not allowed.
Reservation policy: no. **Winter condition:** open, damp.
Terrain: flat some hills. **Tees:** grass. **Temporary greens:** no.
Services: club rentals, candy, small pro shop.
Comments: Short, well kept course that lets you practice your iron play.
Good walking course that does not play very long. Great for the senior golfer.

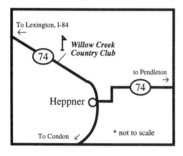

Directions: the golf course is located 1 mile NW of Heppner Oregon off of Hwy 74. The golf course is located on the west side of the Hwy. Look for signs to the golf course that are posted on the Hwy.

Course Yardage & Par:
M-1725 yards, par 30.
W-1725 yards, par 30.
Dual tees 18 holes:
M-3410 yards, par 60.
W-3410 yards, par 60.

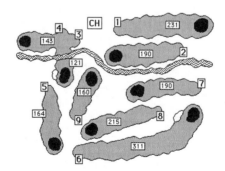

Wilson's Willow Run Executive Golf Course (semi-private)
Wilson Road; Route 1, Box 22; Boardman, OR 97818; (503) 481-4381
Manager: Lois Peterson. 9 hole executive course, dual tees for 18 holes
Rating/Slope: M 55.7/82; W 56.1/79. **Course record:** 57.
Greens fee: W/D $7/$5; W/E $9/$6; no credit cards. **Power cart:** $12/$7.50.
Pull cart: $2/$1. **Trail fee:** $3/$2. **Reservation policy:** yes, suggested on week-
ends, holidays. **Winter condition:** open, but club house closed Dec. 1 - March 1.
Terrain: flat. **Tees:** grass. **Temporary greens:** yes. **Services:** club rentals.
Comments: Very challenging short "easy" course with water hazards and trees.
Course also features "The Wedge" beginners course and practice area.
($1, complimentary prior to tee time.) Course closed Mondays except holidays.

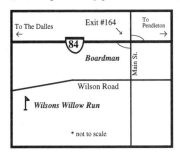

Directions: from I-84 take the Boardman exit #164. Turn left 1 mile to Wilson Road. Turn right and proceed 3 miles to the golf course. The golf course is located at the west end of Wilson Road.

Course Yardage & Par:
M-1803 yards, par 31.
W-1803 yards, par 31.
Dual Tees 18 holes:
M-3742 yards, par 62.
W-3742 yards, par 62.

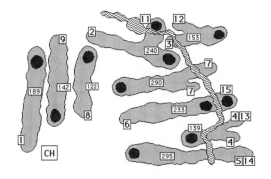

Woodburn Golf Club (public)

Hwy. 214 West; Woodburn, OR 97071; no phone
Pro: none available. 9 hole course.
Rating/Slope: the golf course is not rated. **Course record:** 31.
Greens fee: $2 all day; annual fees $50; husbands & wives $60; no credit cards.
Power cart: none. **Pull cart:** none. **Trail fee:** no charge.
Reservation policy: self service. **Winter condition:** open, wet.
Terrain: flat. **Tees:** grass. **Temporary greens:** no. **Services:** none.
Comments: Mens club plays on Wednesday morning. Ladies club
plays on Thursday morning. One of the last courses in the northwest to have
sand greens. The course can be very wet during the winter months.

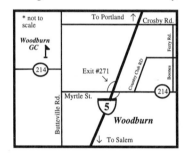

Directions: from I-5 north & south take
the Woodburn exit. Go westbound on
Hwy 214 for 1.9 miles. The golf course
will be on your right hand side.

Course Yardage & Par:
M-2592 yards, par 34.
W-2570 yards, par 36.

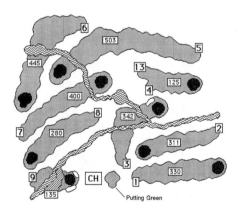

Bay Breeze Golf & D.R. (public)
232 S Latimer Road; Tillamook, OR 97141
(503) 842-1166. Pro: 3 to serve you.
9 hole course, covered driving range.
Course record: 24. Greens fee: $5; Sr. rates.
Pull cart: $1. Terrain: flat. **Tees:** grass.
Services: club rentals, pro shop, deli, beer, range.
Course yardage & par: 822 yards, par 27.
Comments: course features 2 lake holes and large
greens. The facility will feature a driving range
and putting course. Driving Range is now open.
Directions: the course is located on Hwy 101 right
across from the Tillamook Cheese factory on the
east side of the Hwy. Look for signs at your turn.

Map 1; Grid B1

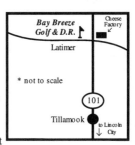

Bayou Golf Club (public)
9301 SW Bayou Dr.; McMinnville, OR 97128
(503) 472-4651. Pro: Sarah Bakefelt.
9 hole course. Course record: 22.
Greens fee: $8/$4. Pull cart: $2/$1. Tees: grass.
Terrain: flat, some hills. **Services:** club rentals,
lessons, snack bar, beer, wine, pro shop, range.
Course yardage/par: M-1020 yards, par 27;
W-985 yards, 27. Comments: excellent facility
with small greens and holes with a variety of
lengths. **Directions:** the course is located 1.25
miles south of McMinnville on Hwy 99. Look
for a large sign along the Hwy.

Map 1; Grid B2

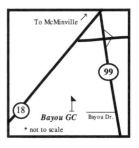

Clear Lake Golf Course (public)
7275 Wheatland Road N; Salem, OR 97303
(503) not listed. Instuctor: N/A.
9 hole course. Course record: 22.
Greens fee: $6.50/$4; Sr. rates.
Pull cart: $1. Terrain: flat. **Tees:** grass.
Services: lessons, snack bar, pro shop.
Course yardage & par: 933 yards, par 27.
Comments: golf course is easy to walk and is
great for seniors. **Directions:** from I-5 take exit
#263 (Brooks-Gervais). Go west on Brookdale
Rd NE for 1.7 miles to Wheatland Road. Turn
left. The golf course will be located 1.8 miles
ahead on your right.

Map 1; Grid C3

Cottonwood Lakes Golf Course (public)
3225 River Road South; Salem, OR 97302
(503) 364-3673. Pro: Alan Olson, PGA.
9 hole course, covered driving range.
Course record: 24. Greens fee: $12/$6. Jr. & Sr.
rates. Pull cart: $1. Terrain: flat. Tees: grass.
Services: club rentals, lessons, snack bar,
pro shop, 50 tee driving range.
Course yardage & par: 1250 yards, par 28.
Comments: challenging golf course.
Directions: from I-5 north take Parkway exit #248
and go north on Commercial to Owens.
Left on Owens to River Road. Left to the golf
course. From I-5 south take exit #253 (Mission).

Map 1; Grid C3

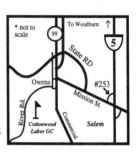

Eagles on the Green (private)
1375 Irving Road; Eugene, OR 97404
(503) 688-9741. Pro: none.
9 hole course. Course record: 23.
Greens fee: private club.
Pull cart: private. **Terrain:** flat.
Tees: grass. **Services:** restauraunt, lounge.
Course yardage & par: 1295 yards, par 27.
Comments: must be an eagle member or
guest of one to play. Good variety of holes.
Directions: from I-5 take Beltline Rd exit.
Proceed west for 4.3 miles to Irving Rd. The
golf course will be located on your right hand
side of the street.

Map 1; Grid D3

Frontier Golf Course (public)
2965 N Holly Street; Canby, OR 97013
(503) 266-4435. Owner: Joe Sisul.
9 hole course. Course record: 24.
Greens fee: $9/$5; Sr. rates. **Power cart:** $5.
Pull cart: $1. **Terrain:** flat. **Tees:** grass.
Services: club rentals, pro shop.
Course yardage & par: 1063 yards, par 27.
Comments: economical golf course. This is a
good facility to take the family to.
Directions: When in Canby on Hwy 99E look
for Ivy St. Proceed 1 block west on Ivy St.
Proceed to Holly St. and turn west. The golf
course will be located 1.8 miles ahead.

Map 1; Grid B4

Golf City (public)
2115 Highway 20; Corvallis, OR 97330
(503) 753-6213. Pro: Dick Mason, PGA.
9 hole course. Course record: 21.
Greens fee: W/D $4.50; W/E $5; M/C, VISA.
Pull cart: none. **Terrain:** flat, some hills.
Tees: grass & mats. **Services:** club rentals,
lessons, snack bar, coffee shop, beer, wine,
pro shop, miniature golf.
Course yardage & par: 801 yards, par 28.
Comments: home of the shortest par 4 on record.
Directions: when entering Corvallis on Hwy 34.
Proceed to Hwy 20 and go eastbound (north to
Albany). The course is located 2.1 miles ahead .

Map 1; Grid C3

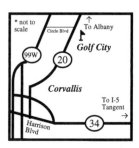

Hillebrand's Paradise Ranch Resort (public)
7000 D Monument Dr; Grants Pass, OR 97526
(503) 479-4333. Owner: Herbert Hillebrand.
3 hole course. Course record: 25.
Greens fee: $5/$3 guests; $7/$4 others.
Pull cart: none. **Terrain:** flat. **Tees:** grass.
Services: pop machine, resort area.
Course yardage & par: 1310 yards, par 27.
Comments: short three hole course, set in a
very quiet area of of Oregon. Good greens.
Directions: From I-5 N&S take exit #61. Turn
left at the stop sign off the ramp. Go under
freeway, right at light, which is Monument Dr.
Proceed for 2 miles to the Inn and the course.

Map 1; Grid G4

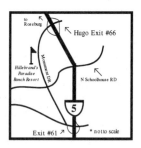

Northwest Aluminum Golf Club (private)
3313 West 2nd; The Dalles, OR 97058
(503) 296-6161. Pro: none.
9 hole course. Course record: 24.
Greens fee: private club, members only.
Pull cart: private. **Terrain:** flat, some hills.
Tees: grass. **Services:** private club.
Course yardage & par: 1183 yards, par 27.
Comments: good walking golf course.
Directions: From I-84 east & West exit at The
Dalles. Proceed north to 2nd St and turn west-
bound. Follow 2nd to the golf course, which
will be located on your right hand side.

Map 2; Grid B3

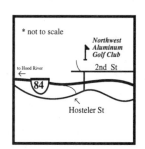

82nd Avenue Range
2806 NE 82nd; Portland, OR 97220
(503) 253-0902. Pro: Chuck Milne, PGA.
Hours: M-F 9am-11pm, Sat. & Sun 7am-11pm.
Lights: yes. **Covered:** yes.
Putting & chipping: yes. **Services:** club repair,
lessons, pro shop. **Directions:** I-205 N&S take
airport exit and travel westbound to 82nd. Turn
left on 82nd and proceed to the driving range.
<u>Map 1; Grid B4</u>

Caddieshack Driving Range
5201 State Street; Salem, OR 97301
(503) 581-7045. Pro: Jim Hynds, PGA.
Hours: 8:30am to dusk. **Lights:** no.
Covered: no. **Putting & chipping:** no.
Services: lessons, vending machines.
Directions: from I-5 take the Center St exit and
travel east. At Lancaster turn right and follow to
State St. Turn left on State St and proceed to the
driving range. <u>Map 1; Grid C3</u>

Cordon Road Driving Range
4205 Cordon Road NE; Salem, OR 97302
(503) 362-3694. Pro: Mike Dwyer, PGA.
Hours: seasonal hours. **Lights:** N/A.
Covered: yes. **Putting & chipping:** yes.
Services: lessons, club repair, pro shop, sand
bunker. **Directions:** the driving range is located
1/2 mile north of the Silverton Road and Cordon
Road intersection.   <u>Map 1; Grid C3</u>

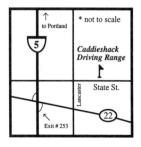

Cottonwood Lakes G. C. & Driving Range
3225 River Road South; Salem, OR 97302
(503) 364-3673. Pro: Alan Olson, PGA.
Hours: please call for specific hours. **Lights:** N/A.
Covered: yes, 50 tees. **Putting & chipping:** yes.
Services: club rentals, lessons, snack bar, pro shop,
9 hole par 28 course. **Directions:** from I-5 northbound take Parkway exit #248 and go north on
Commercial to Owens. Turn left on Owens to River
Road. Left to the range. From I-5 southbound take
exit #253 (Mission).   <u>Map ; Grid C3</u>

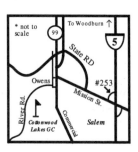

Dino's Driving Range
21661 Beavercreek RD; Oregon City, OR 97045
(503) 632-3986. Owner: Dino Marasigan.
Hours: W/D 9am-dusk; W/E 8am-dusk. **Lights:** no.
Covered: no. **Putting & Chipping:** putting only.
Services: small pro shop, 2 teaching pros, lessons.
Directions: from I-205 N&S take exit #10 (Park
Place). Head south on Hwy 213. Turn left (east)
at Beavercreek RD (third light).The range is located
ahead. **Map 1; Grid B4**

Eagle Driving Range
63977 Imnaha Hwy; Joseph, OR 97946
(503) 432-4001. Pro: N/A
Hours: 7am to dark March-November.
Lights: yes. **Covered:** no.
Putting & chipping: yes, with practice bunker.
Services: lessons, small pro shop.
Directions: the driving range is located 1/2 mile
out of Joseph, Oregon on the north side of the
Imnaha Highway. **Map 3; Grid B4**

Grants Pass Golf Center
2450 NW Vine Street; Grant Pass, OR 97526
(503) 479-9500. Pro: Tommy Smith.
Hours: 9 am to 10pm. **Lights:** yes.
Covered: yes. **Putting & chipping:** yes.
Services: club rentals, lessons, club repair, pro shop.
Directions: from I-5 southbound take the first
Grants Pass exit (last going northbound). Turn right
at the first light. Proceed to Vine St and then turn
right on Vine St. **Map 1; Grid G4**

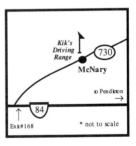

Kik's Driving Range
off of Hwy 730; McNary, OR 97882
(503) 922-2844. Pro: Todd Sprong.
Hours: please call for hours summer hours.
Lights: information not available.
Covered: information not available.
Putting & chipping: information not available.
Services: lessons, small pro shop.
Directions: the range is located in the town of
McNary Oregon off of Hwy 730. **Map 2; Grid B4**

Raymax Driving Range
3707 Aberlein; Klamath Falls, OR 97603
(503) 883-2143. Pro: none.
Hours: dawn to dusk, call for hours.
Lights: information not available.
Covered: information not available.
Putting & chipping: information not available.
Services: limited services.
Directions: the range is located in Klamath Falls,
Oregon on Aberlein Street. **Map 2; Grid G2**

Sah-Hah-Lee Golf Course & Driving Range
17104 SE 130th Avenue; Clackamas, OR 97015
(503) 655-3215. Pro: Don Otto, PGA.
Hours: 6:30am-9pm (summer); 8-6:30pm (winter).
Lights: yes. **Covered:** yes. **Putting & chipping:** yes.
Services: club repair, private & group lessons,
snack bar, pro shop, 18 hole par 3 golf course.
Directions: from I-205 N&S exit at Hwy 212
going eastbound. Proceed to SE 130th Ave.Turn.
right. Head south to the range. **Map 1; Grid B4**

Sunset Golf Center
16251 SW Jenkins Road; Beaverton, OR 97006
(503) 626-2244; Manager: N/A.
Hours: W/D 9am-9pm winter; extended W/E and
summer hours. **Lights:** yes. **Covered:** yes. **Putting
& chipping:** yes. **Services:** grass tees, mini golf,
lessons, pro shop, deli, club repair, practice bunker.
Directions: from Hwy 217 take the Walker RD exit.
Head west turn left on Cedar Hills RD. Proceed to
Jenkins turn right. Follow to range. **Map 1; Grid B4**

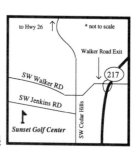

Tualatin Island Greens Driving Range *New*
20400 SW Cipole RD; Tualatin, OR 97062
(503) 691-8400. Pro: Todd Andrews, PGA.
Hours: 7am-10pm (summer); 8am-9pm (winter).
Lights: yes. **Covered:** yes & heated stalls.
Putting & chipping: yes. **Services:** club repair, 18
hole putting course, snack bar, pro shop, lessons.
Directions: from I-5 N&S exit #289 (Hwy 212)
going westbound on Tualatin-Sherwood Road for 3
miles to Cipole Road. Turn north. **Map 1; Grid B4**

Westside Driving Range
6050 Hwy 22; Independence, OR 97351
(503) 364-3615. Owner: Paul Cheney.
Hours: open daylight hours.
Lights: no. **Covered:** yes.
Putting & chipping: yes.
Services: club repair, lessons, pro shop, sand trap.
Directions: the range is located between Salem
and Independence Oregon right off of Hwy 22.
Look for the signs to the range. **Map 1; Grid C3**

A & A Custom Golf
4803 SW 76th; Portland, Oregon; (503) 292-3711
Services: club repair, custom clubs, refinishing.

A Hole in One Golf Shop
2300 NE Division; Bend, Oregon; (503) 388-7537
Services: club repair, custom clubs, club refinishing, swing analysis.

All Seasons Sports
714 Main Street; Klamath Falls, Oregon; (503) 884-3863
Services: retail store.

Caplan Sportsworld
625 SW 4th & Morrison; Portland, Oregon; (503) 226-6467 or 800-CAPLAN5
Services: retail golf store, custom clubs.

Cascade Custom Golf
14980 S Blue Vista Drive; Oregon City, Oregon; (503) 650-9522
Services: club repairs, custom clubs, club refinishing.

Club Doctor, The
7846 Battle Creek Road SE; Salem, Oregon; (503) 362-1566
Services: club repair, custom clubs, club refinishing.

Custom Golf by Stu
17110 NE Halsey; Gresham, Oregon; (503) 255-8280
Services: custom clubs.

Dot Golf Center
14624 SE McLoughlin Blvd.; Milwaukie, Oregon; (503) 794-0940
Services: club repair, custom clubs, club refinishing.

Dot Golf Center
8604 SW Hall Boulevard; Beaverton, Oregon; (503) 641-9525
Services: club repair, custom clubs, club refinishing.

Double Eagle Golf Center
8200 SW Scholls Ferry Road; Beaverton, Oregon; (503) 646-5166
Services: club repair, custom clubs, club refinishing, lessons.

Entrepreneurial Golf
PO Box 566; Gresham, Oregon 97030; (503) 666-3152
Services: Golf accessories, prints, tee prizes.

Foltz's Valley Golf Service
5239 Table Rock Road; Central Point, Oregon; (503) 664-3971
Services: club repair, custom clubs, refinishing, custom fitting, used clubs.

Golf USA
3665 SW Cedar Hills Boulevard; Beaverton, Oregon; (503) 526-9218
Services: club repair, custom clubs, refinishing, lessons, nationwide shipping.

Golf USA
2285 Lancaster Drive NE: Salem, Oregon; (503) 375-6203
Services: retail store, swing analyzer.

Golf USA Sport Tech Swing
2061 Roberts Road; Medford, Oregon; (503) 776-1370
Services: lessons.

Golf City
1052 NE 3rd Street; Bend, Oregon; (503) 389-3919
Services: club repair, custom clubs, club refinishing.

Golf Crafters, The
1831 NE Stephens; Roseburg, Oregon; (503) 673-2868
Services: lessons, club repair, custom clubs, retail store.

Golf Den, The
7320 SW Beaverton Hillsdale Highway; Portland, Oregon; (503) 292-6520
Services: club repair, club refinishing, retail merchandise, large pro shop.

Golf Den, The
12433-B NE Glisan; Portland, Oregon; (503) 255-5549
Services: club repair, club refinishing, retail merchandise, large pro shop.

Golf Swing Shop
2061 Roberts Road; Medford, Oregon; (503) 776-3053
Services: lessons.

Golfers Garage
34 Carthage; Eugene, Oregon; (503) 688-3754
Services: club repair, custom clubs, new & used clubs.

Hank Childs Golf Shop
2200 NE 71st; Portland, Oregon; (503) 253-4744
Services: club repair, club refinishing, lessons.

Huff's Golf Shop
5051 NW Garden Valley Road; Roseburg, Oregon; (503) 672-4041
Services: club repair, retail shop, lessons.

International Discount Golf
2806 NE 82nd; Portland, Oregon; (503) 253-0902
Services: retail store, lessons, club fitting, driving range.

International Discount Golf
11493 SE 82nd; Portland, Oregon; (503) 659-4653
Services: retail store, lessons, club fitting.

International Discount Golf
9315 SW Beaverton Hillsdale Highway; Portland, Oregon; (503) 292-5446
Services: retail store, lessons, club fitting.

Jack Beaudoins Golf Shop
1459 NE Burnside; Gresham, Oregon; (503) 666-GOLF
Services: club regripping, repair, lessons, club fitting.

Kangaroo Golf
3988 SE 82nd Avenue; Portland, Oregon; (503) 777-0650
Services: not available.

Las Vegas Discount Golf & Tennis
61249 S Hwy 97, Unit A; Bend, Oregon; (503) 383-2944
Services: retail golf store.

Laurel Ridge Golf Company
Grants Pass, Oregon; (503) 476-8929
Services: full service club repairs, custom clubs.

Lumpy's Pro Golf Discount
1341 NE 3rd; Bend, Oregon; (503) 385-5779
Services: club repair, custom clubs, club refinishing, retail merchandise.

Marvins Golf Town
808 E Main; Klamath Falls, Oregon; (503) 884-1493
Services: club repair, refinishing.

Missing Link, The
1707 N Highway 97; Redmond, Oregon; (503) 923-3426
Services: club repair, custom clubs, club refinishing.

Mulligan's Golf Equipment Liquidators
11040 SW Allen; Beaverton, Oregon; (503) 644-9906
Services: golf closeout merchandise, consignments welcome

Nevada Bob's
101215 SW Parkway; Portland, Oregon; (503) 297-1808
Services: club repair, custom clubs, club refinishing, retail merchandise.

Nevada Bob's
11211 SE 82nd Avenue; Portland, Oregon; (503) 653-7202
Services: club repair, custom clubs, club refinishing, retail merchandise.

Northwoods
7410 SW Macadam; Portland, Oregon; (503) 245-1910
Services: club repair, custom clubs, club refinishing.

Parfection
1293 NE 3rd; Bend, Oregon; (503) 389-3499
Services: club repair, custom clubs, club refinishing, lessons, retail merchandise.

Portland Golf Academy
8103 NE Killingsworth; Portland, Oregon; (503) 253-4653
Services: club repair, custom clubs, club refinishing, lessons.

Portland Golf Outlet
321 SW 4th; Portland, Oregon; (503) 228-7848
Services: custom clubs, hitting net, retail store.

Prescription Golf
12014 SE Division; Portland, Oregon; (503) 760-1222
Services: club repair, custom clubs, lessons, swing analysis.

Pro Golf Discount
9555 SW Cascade Avenue; Beaverton, Oregon; (503) 646-8673
Services: club repair, custom clubs, club refinishing, retail merchandise.

S-2 Oregon
725 SW 56th Street; Corvallis, Oregon; (503) 752-8649
Services: not available.

Wooden Touch Putters
PO Box 457; 1125 S 1st; Coos Bay, Oregon; (503) 267-7804
Services: custom putters.

Auburn Center Golf Club; 5220 Center Street NE; Salem, OR
(503) 363-4404; see page 11
Rates: the golf course offers special senior rates throughout the week.
The normal weekday rates are only $10 for 18 holes and $6 for 9 holes.
Terrain: the golf course is very flat. **Trail fee:** not allowed.
Comments: this is a very moderate short executive length golf course with a
par of 29 if you want to play something different for a very low price.

Charbonneau Golf &CC; 32020 Charbonneau Drive; Wilsonville, OR
(503) 694-1246; see page 25
Rates: this golf course could be one of the best kept secrets in the state for under
$25. If you don't mind a little higher priced golf course this will be worth the price
of admission. Normal fees are $22 and well worth it. **Terrain:** flat, some hills.
Trail fee: not allowed. **Comments:** this is a 27 hole executive length course that
is fairly easy to walk. you will find several ponds and beautiful tree lined fairways.
Worth a trip if in the area.

Claremont Golf Club; 15955 NW West Union Road; Portland, OR
(503) 690-4589; see page 28
Rates: the golf course offers special senior rates throughout the week (Monday-
Friday). Great price on a public course with some personality. **Terrain:** flat, very
easy walking course that is not at all a back breaker. **Trail fee:** not allowed.
Comments: this 9 hole track sports dual tees for those wanting to play a full 18
hole round. Great test of golf with water coming into play on several holes.

Echo Hills Golf Course; 100 Golf Course Road; Echo, OR
(503) 376-8244; see page 45
Rates: the golf course offers special senior rates throughout the week. The greens
fee are weekdays $12 for eighteen holes and $6 for nine holes. On the weekends
they will run $16 for eighteen holes and $8 for nine holes. **Terrain:** the golf course
is very hilly so I recommend renting a power cart for your round. **Trail fee:** $3.
Comments: challenging course that will offer the senior golfer with a real test.

Fiddler's Green Golf Course & Driving Range; 91292 Hwy 99 N; Eugene, OR
(503) 689-8464; see page 50
Rates: the golf course offers special senior rates throughout the week. The greens
fee are $5 for 18 holes and $3.50 for 9 holes. **Terrain:** the golf course is very flat
and easy to walk. **Trail fee:** not available. **Comments:** if you want to play a good
golf course but don't want to play at the regulation length I would recommend this
course. All 18 holes of this par 3 layout will challenge you. You cannot beat the
price either. Stop by the pro shop after your round, they have everything you could
imagine having to do with golf. The course boasts that it has one of the biggest on
course pro shops in the world. You will find great bargains.

Harbor Links Golf Course; 601 Harbor Isles Boulevard; Klamath Falls, OR
(503) 882-0609; see page 60
Rates: the golf course offers special winter rates and is one of the only golf courses in the area. The normal rates are W/D $20 and W/E $23. **Terrain:** flat and is very easy to walk. **Trail fee:** not allowed. **Comments:** excellent golf course with a very demanding layout. Lakes will come into play on several different holes throughout the golf couse putting an emphais on your shot placement.

Heron Lakes Golf Club; 3500 N Victory Boulevard; Portland, OR
(503) 289-1818; see pages 62-63
Rates: no real senior rates for the Great Blue Course but the golf course normal rates are a real bargain.The Greenback does offer a senior discount **Terrain:** the golf course is very flat and easy to walk. **Trail fee:** $4/$2. **Comments:** this complex has over 36 holes of championship golf. The Great Blue course is one of the toughest golf courses in the state of Oregon, so if you really want to challenge yourself this is it. With many sets of tees, you can play from the back or play a shorter course of championship caliber. This golf course is worth a special trip if you are in the greater Portland area.

KAH-NEE-TA Resort Course; 100 Main Street; Warm Springs, OR
800-831-0100; see page 73
Rates: the golf course offers senior discount rates during the week. The normal greens fee prices are $30 for 18 holes and $18 for 9 holes. **Terrain:** the golf course is an easy walking course with very flat terrain. **Trail fee:** $7.
Comments: this a great golf course in central Oregon that is very special. If you want sunshine and great golf this is the place to go. Course closed in the winter.

The Knolls Golf Club; 1919 Recreation Lane; Sutherlin, OR
(503) 459-4422; see page 78
Rates: the golf course offers special rates for the senior golfer (Friday only).
Terrain: lots of rolling hills. **Trail fee:** $3. **Comments:** great golf course that has undergone a lot of changes that make it a first rate course. If you are traveling by RV the golf course has plenty of parking available. The course is a links style course that has plenty of personality. This is worth the trip if in the area.

Mountain View Golf Course; 27195 SE Kelso Road; Boring, OR
(503) 663-4869; see page 98
Rates: this course offers the senior golfer special rates off what is already a very affordable green fee $17 (on the weekdays). **Terrain:** the golf course is fairly level with some hills coing into play on certain areas of the course. The track is walkable however. **Trail fee:** 1/2 of the power cart rental $20. **Comments:** good public golf course that is not overly long from the middle tee. The facility has a very good restaurant and lounge area for your after golf relaxation.

Neskowin Beach Golf Course; Hawk Creek Avenue; Neskowin, OR
(503) 392-3377; see page 99
Rates: the golf course offers special rates for the senior golfer. Terrain: the golf
course is very flat and easy to walk. **Trail fee:** $3 (a bargin for those owning
personal carts). **Comments:** If you are looking for friendly golf course that is
very affordable while you are visiting the Oregon Coast try Neskowin Beach.
You will not be disappointed.

Ocean Dunes Golf Links; 3345 Munsel Lake Road; Florence, OR
(503) 997-3232; see page 104
Rates: the golf course special senior rates during the week. The normal greens fee
are $28 for 18 holes and $15 for 9 holes. **Terrain:** the golf course is relatively
flat and is easy to walk. **Trail fee:** $8. **Comments:** this golf course is built in a
fantastic setting on the Oregon coast. If you are looking to play a real links type
golf course this is the one for you. The golf course stays very dry during the
winter months because it was actually built on the sand dunes. Great golf course.

Progress Downs Golf Course; 8200 Scholls Ferry Road; Beaverton, OR
(503) 646-5166; see page 118
Rates: the golf course offers special rates for the senior golfer during the week.
Terrain: the golf course has some hills but is definitely not a back breaker.
Trail fee: the trail fee is only $3, a great bargain if you own your own golf cart.
Comments: good public golf course that has a great on course pro shop and
driving range. The course is not overly long but can play tight in spots.

Vernonia Golf Club; 15961 Timber Road East; Vernonia, OR
(503) 429-6811; see page 172
Rates: the golf course offers special rates for the senior golfer during the weekdays only. **Terrain:** the golf course is flat in spots with some rolling hills
throughout the layout. This course is very walkable. **Trail fee:** the trail fee is only
$4 for personal carts. **Comments:** this 9 hole track just keeps getting better and
better every year. Look for Vernonia to be expanding it's layout to a full 18 holes
in the near future.

Wildwood Golf Course; 21281 NW Saint Helens Road; Portland, OR
(503) 621-3402; see page 176
Rates: the golf course does not offer special rates for the senior golfer during the
week but the green fees are very affordable. **Terrain:** the course does have some
hills to contend with but for bargin green fees it is not a real back breaker.
Trail fee: the trail fee is only $3 for personal carts. **Comments:** this friendly
course offers a real family feeling while playing it. If you are looking for a course
near the Portland metropolitan area try Wildwood.

Our newest section in *Golfing in Oregon* is called **Weekend Getaways.** We have received calls from people using the book for suggestions on weekend trips and my family and I personally enjoy going golfing in the morning and seeing other attractions in the afternoon. We have designed this section, therefore, to give you some ideas of short weekend trips you could take in the area and you can tailor them to your taste! Any further information you would like on specific lodging availability the Chamber of Commerce in the destination city would be eager to provide. Some of our suggestions may be seasonal so it is always best to call ahead.

Gearhart/Seaside: One of the most popular spots on the Oregon coast has three golf courses to choose from: The Highlands at Gearhart, Gearhart Golf Links, and Seaside Golf Course. Lodging is available in both oceanside towns. Besides beachcombing and taking in the magnificent beauty of the Oregon coast there are many other attractions. Seaside offers extensive gift shopping, arcades, and dining. Just a short drive south on Hwy 101 will take you to the quaint town of Cannon Beach. Here you will find dining, gallery and gift shopping as well as the famous "Haystack Rock" on the beach. During the summer months Cannon Beach is host to a world famous sandcastle building contest you won't want to miss.

Grants Pass/Medford: Southwestern Oregon is home to a number of unique natural attractions which would make for a wonderful afternoon trip after your round of golf. This area is also has three new golf courses to play: Dutcher Creek (Grants Pass), Stewart Meadows and Quail Point (Medford). The other courses available are Bear Creek and Cedar Links. Both Grants Pass and Medford have plenty of lodging and dining available. Just a short distance from both cities lies the Oregon Caves National Monument. The caves are usually open year round with guided tours. If you enjoy a scenic drive Crater Lake National Park is northeast of both cities. The 1,962 foot deep lake is an awesome specimen of volcanic activity from the past. There is a drive you can take that circles the rim of the crater with viewpoints along the way. A lodge and food services are available (seasonal). For the real adventurist the Rogue River offers whitewater rafting trips.

Portland: The thriving metropolis of Portland and its suburbs offer a myriad of golf courses to play. Portland itself has world class dining and lodging available. After your round of golf you might enjoy visiting the International Rose Gardens or take the drive east on I-84 to the Columbia River Gorge. This scenic area offers extensive hiking trails including one to Multnomah Falls, the highest waterfall in the state. Mt. Hood is only a short drive east of Portland as well. The mountain is open for snow skiing even in the summer months on the glacier at the upper elevation. Timberline Lodge, a national historic landmark is also located at Mt. Hood and is well worth the drive to visit. Portland also offers downtown shopping and a scenic park on the Willamette River which runs through the city. The city and surrounding areas offer many museums which concentrate on the historic Oregon Trail. East of I-5 between Portland and Eugene is the Oregon wine country where many of the wineries are open for vineyard tours and wine tasting. Visitor centers provide information on all these various attractions.

Salishan/Gleneden Beach: The Salishan Resort is excellent for a weekend getaway on the beautiful Oregon coast. The resort offers an exquisite restaurant featuring northwest cuisine along with championship golf.

Sisters: Located in central Oregon this area will remind you of the Ponderosa. Black Butte (10 mi west of Sisters) is a full service resort with horseback riding, 2 championship golf courses on site, fine dining, grocery store, tennis, swimming and supervised childrens activities. Sisters also has lodging and dining available. After your golf game there are many things to interest you. Sisters is designed to look like an old western town with many small shops to explore. Others might enjoy an afternoon hike up Black Butte or drive to the Lava fields at the summit of McKenzie Pass which include a round tower made of the volcanic rock. At the top of the tower there are observation windows which view each of the many mountain tops in the area. There is also an interpretive trail through the lava fields. Just a short drive east of Sisters is Redmond where Eagle Crest Resort is located. This resort also offers two championship caliber golf courses on site. Other amenities include tennis, pool and jacuzzi, nature and bike trails, childcare, a massage, aerobics, and tanning salon, equestrian center, and fine dining. Also in the area is Crooked River Ranch GC that recently expanded to a full 18 holes.

Sunriver: The Sunriver Resort is also a full service resort offering fine dining, lodging, swimming, shopping, boutiques, and two championship golf courses with a third scheduled to open in 1995 called Crosswater. This private club will reciprocate with Sunriver lodge guests and promises to be a truly spectacular addition to the central Oregon golf scene. Other attractions in the area include the High Desert Museum. This features wildlife, an interpretive center, and a replica of the early settlers homes and a sawmill. Lava Butte (11 miles south of Bend) offers self-guided trails and lava tubes which you can hike in for up to 1 mile. Bring warm clothes and a flashlight (or you can rent a Coleman lantern). The lava tubes are quite cool, even in the summer months.

Welches: Since 1893 The Resort at the Mountain has been catering to the public. First founded near the Oregon Trail, this area is rich in history and natural beauty. Previously known as "Rippling River Resort" the name has been changed to The Resort at the Mountain and extensive re-modeling has taken place. Located at the foot of Mount Hood this is truly an all season resort. Offering 27 challenging holes of golf in an alpine setting is just the beginning for this getaway. The resort also features 160 luxury guest rooms, (some with fireplaces), a complete fitness center, 6 tennis courts, a pool and jacuzzi, 2 restaurants, hiking, biking, volleyball, basket-ball, croquet, basketball, badmiton, and gift shops. The Mt. Hood and Columbia River Gorge Recreation areas offer guided fishing trips, trout farm fishing for children, river rafting on the Deschutes River, wind surf-ing, go cart rentals, and much, much, more.

Oregon is a beautiful state with many activities to offer in conjunction with golf. If you desire further information on a specific area or activity the Oregon State Tourism Office will help you.

Call: 1-800-547-7842 (outside Oregon) or 1-800-233-3306 (within Oregon).

Albany: The Golf Club of Oregon, Springhill.
Ashland: Oak Knoll.
Astoria: Astoria G & C.C.
Aurora: Langdon Farms.
Baker City: Baker Golf Club.
Bandon: Bandon Face Rock.
Banks: Quail Valley.
Beaverton: Progress Downs, Sunset Golf Center.
Bend: Awbrey Glen, Bend G & C.C., Black Butte Ranch, Broken Top, Crosswater, Mountain High, Orion Greens, Pine Meadows C.C., River's Edge, Sunriver Resort.
Blue River: Tokatee.
Boardman: Wilson's Willow Run.
Boring: Greenlea, Mountain View.
Canby: Frontier, Willamette Valley
Cave Junction: Illinois Valley.
Christmas Valley: Christmas Valley.
Clackamas: Pleasant Valley, Sah-hah-lee.
Condon: Condon.
Coos Bay/North Bend: Coos Bay C.C., Kentuck, Sunset Bay.
Cornelius: Forest Hills G.C., Pumpkin Ridge.
Corvallis: Corvallis, Golf City, Marysville, Trysting Tree.
Cottage Grove: Hidden Valley, Middlefield Village.
Creswell: Emerald Valley.
Crooked River: Crooked River Ranch.
Dallas: Sandstrip.
The Dalles: The Dalles Country Club, Northwest Aluminum Golf Club, Lone Pine Village Golf Course & Driving Range.
Dundee: Riverwood.
Eagle Creek: Eagle Creek.
Echo: Echo Hills.
Enterprise: Alpine Meadows.
Estacada: Springwater.
Eugene: Eugene C.C., Fiddlers Green, Laurelwood, Oakway, Riveridge, Eagles on the Green.
Florence: Ocean Dunes, Sandpines Golf Resort.
Forest Grove: Sunset Grove.
Fossil: Kinzua Hills.
Gearhart: Gearhart Links, The Highlands.
Gladstone: Rivergreens.
Glenden Beach: Salishan.
Gold Beach: Cedar Bend.
Gold Hill: Laurel Hill.

Grants Pass: Colonial Valley, Dutcher Creek, Grants Pass, Hillebrand's Paradise Ranch Resort, Mulligan Driving Range, Red Mountain G.C.
Gresham: Gresham GC, Persimmon G&CC.
Heppner: Willow Creek CC.
Hines: Valley GC.
Hillsboro: Meriwether National, Kilarney West, Orenco Woods.
Hood River: Hood River, Indian Creek.
Independence: Oak Knoll, West Side.
John Day: John Day G.C.
Joseph: Eagle Driving Range.
Junction City: Shadow Hills.
King City: King City.
Klamath Falls: Harbor Links, Reames, Round Lake, Raymax GC, Sheild Crest.
La Grande: La Grande CC.
La Pine: Quail Run.
Lakeview: Lakeridge.
Lake Oswego: Lake Oswego, Oswego Lake.
Leaburg: McKenzie River.
Lebanon: Pineway.
Lincoln City: Lakeside G&RC.
Lyons: Elkhorn Valley.
McMinnville: Bayou, Michelbook.
Madras: Nine Peaks.
Manzanita: Manzanita.
McNary: Kik's Driving Range.
Medford: Bear Creek, Cedar Links, Quail Point, Rogue Valley C.C., Stewart Meadows, Stoneridge.
Milton-Freewater: Milton-Freewater.
Mollala: Arrowhead.
Mount Angel: Evergreen.
Mulino: Ranch Hills.
Myrtle Point: Coquille Valley.
Neskowin: Hawk Creek, Neskowin Beach.
Newport: Agate Beach.
Oakridge: Circle Bar.
Ontario: Shadow Butte.
Oregon City: Dino's Driving Range, Oregon City.
Pendleton: Pendleton.
Portland: Broadmoor, Columbia-Edgewater, Claremont, Colwood, Dino's, Eastmoreland, Glendoveer, Heron Lakes, Jim Colbert's Hound Hollow, Portland, Portland Meadows, Progress Downs, Riverside, Rock Creek, Rose City, Sunset Golf Center, Top O'Scott, Waverly, Wildwood, 82nd Avenue Driving Range.

Prineville: Meadow Lakes, Prineville.
Redmond: Eagle Crest Resort, Eagle Ridge, Juniper.
Reedsport: Forest Hills.
Roseburg: Roseburg, Roseburg VA, Stewart Park.
Salem: Auburn Center, Battle Creek, Caddieshack, Clear Lake,
Cordon Road Driving Range,Cottonwood Lakes, Creekside G&CC,
Illahe Hills, Meadowlawn, McNary GC, Salem Golf Club, Salemtowne.
Seaside: Seaside.
Sisters: Black Butte Ranch.
Springfield: Springfield.
Stayton: Santiam.
Sunriver: Crosswater, Sunriver Golf Resort.
Sutherlin: The Knolls Golf Club.
Tigard: King City, Summerfield.
Tillamook: Alderbrook, Bay Breeze.
Toledo: Olalla Valley.
Tualatin: Tualatin, Tualatin Greens Driving Range.
Umatilla: Umatilla.
Vernonia: Vernonia.
Waldport: Crestview Hills.
Walterville: McKenzie River.
Warm Springs: KAH-NEE-TA.
Warren: Saint Helens.
Warrenton: Astoria.
Welches: Resort @ the Mountain.
West Linn: Sandelie, The Oregon Golf Club.
White City: Veterans.
Wilsonville: Charbonneau.
Wood Village: Jim Colbert's Hound Hollow.
Woodburn: Senior Estates, The OGA Members Course @ Tukwila,
Woodburn.

Order Form Information

Please send:

_____ *Golfing in Washington $9.95 ea*................. _____
with layouts, map grids and detailed golf course information.

_____ *Golfing in Oregon $8.95 ea*......................... _____
with layouts, map grids and detailed golf course information.

_____ *Golfing in Idaho & Montana** $7.95ea*..... _____
with layouts, map grids and detailed golf course information.

_____ *Golfing in British Columbia** $9.95 ea*.... _____
with layouts, map grids and detailed golf course information.

_____ *Golf Courses of the Pacific N.W. $19.95 ea*... _____
A book covering the unique aspects and history of over
500 golf courses in the Pacific Northwest. By **Jeff Shelley**

_____ *The Northwest Golfers Almanac $7.95 ea*.... _____
Bits and pieces of northwest golf history, golf stories and facts.
A must for any golf historian. Published by **Fairgreens Media**

**due out in
October 1995.   **Add $1.75 per book for postage & handling** _____

Add $2.50 for Canadian Funds...................... _____
(please send US funds)
                    Total Enclosed................ _____

Washington residents add 8.2% for sales tax

<u>**Send Check or Money order to:**</u>
Mac Productions
PO Box 655
Carnation, WA 98014 USA

M
A C **Productions**
Golf Guides Since 1986

Send to:

_____

Name of Recipient

_____

Address

_____

City, State or Province, zip or postal code